S0-ASO-877

THE GOSPEL OF LIFE
AND
THE VISION OF HEALTH CARE

Contributors to this Volume

Helen M. Alvaré, J.D., M.A.
Director of Planning & Information
National Conference of Catholic Bishops
Washington, D.C.

Rev. Benedict Ashley, O.P.
Professor of Sacred Theology
Aquinas Institute of Theology
St. Louis, Missouri

Rev. Ignazio Carrasco de Paula
Institute of Bioethics
Catholic University of the Sacred Heart
Rome, Italy

Peter J. Cataldo, Ph.D.
Director of Research
Pope John XXIII Medical-Moral
Research and Education Center
Braintree, Massachusetts

Michael F. Collins, M.D., F.A.C.P.
President
Caritas Christi Health Care System
Brighton, Massachusetts

T. Murphy Goodwin, M.D.
Assistant Professor
Division of Maternal-Fetal Medicine
University of Southern California
Medical Center
Los Angeles, California

The Most Rev. Alfred C. Hughes, S.T.D.
Bishop of Baton Rouge
Baton Rouge, Louisiana

The Most Rev. James T. McHugh, S.T.D.
Bishop of Camden
Camden, New Jersey

Rev. Brian Mullady, O.P.
Holy Apostles Seminary
Cromwell, Connecticut

Rev. Msgr. James J. Mulligan, S.T.L.
Mary Immaculate Seminary
Northampton, Pennsylvania

Joseph J. Piccione, J.D.
Corporate Ethicist
Corporate Director of Mission Services
OSF Healthcare System
Peoria, Illinois

The Most Rev. Elio Sgreccia
Institute of Bioethics
Catholic University of the Sacred Heart
Rome, Italy

Rev. Russell E. Smith, S.T.D.
President
Pope John XXIII Medical-Moral
Research and Education Center
Braintree, Massachusetts

THE GOSPEL OF LIFE
AND
THE VISION OF HEALTH CARE

Proceedings of the
Fifteenth Workshop for Bishops
Dallas, Texas

Russell E. Smith
Editor

The Pope John Center

Nihil Obstat: Rev. James A. O'Donohoe, J.C.D.

Imprimatur: Bernard Cardinal Law

Date: October 10, 1996

The Nihil Obstat and Imprimatur are a declaration that a book or pamphlet is considered to be free from doctrinal or moral error. It is not implied that those who have granted the Nihil Obstat and Imprimatur agree with the contents, opinions or statements expressed.

©1996 by The Pope John XXIII Medical-Moral Research and Education Center, Braintree, Massachusetts

LIBRARY OF CONGRESS CATALOGING-IN-PUBLICATION DATA

Workshop for Bishops of the United States and Canada (15th : 1996 : Dallas, Tex.)
    The gospel of life and the vision of health care : proceedings of the Fifteenth Bishops' Workshop, Dallas, Texas / Russell E. Smith, editor.
      p. cm.
    Includes bibliographical references.
    ISBN 0-935372-40-7 (pbk)
    1. Medicine–Religious aspects–Catholic Church–Congresses. 2. Medical ethics–Congresses. 3. Christian ethics–Catholic authors–Congresses. I. Smith, Russell E. (Russell Edward) II. Title.
R725.56.W67   1996   96-46483
261.8'321'08822–dc21   CIP

Contents

A Year of Transitions

This year has been a time of a lot of activity at the Pope John Center. The Board of Directors and staff have been preparing for the Center's twenty-fifth anniversary, which will take place throughout 1997 and into early 1998. In addition to the Sixteenth Bishops' Workshop in Dallas, there are plans for expanding the national presence of the Center through special events in various cities, and a change in the format of this volume.

In addition to the programmatic changes, there has been a significant change in leadership of the Center as well. John Haas, formerly the John Cardinal Krol Professor of Moral Theology at St. Charles Borromeo Seminary in Philadelphia, has become the Center's fifth full-time President. I have become Professor of Moral Theology and Coordinator of the Pre-Theology Program at Mount Saint Mary's Seminary in Emmitsburg.

The Present Volume

In the past, the Center has published a volume containing the Proceedings of the Bishops' Workshop in Dallas. The celebration of the Center's twenty-fifth jubilee provides a good occasion to further refine this publication. In the future, the Center will publish selected lectures presented at the workshop as well as other articles originally published in foreign languages and invited works related to moral theology or bioethics. In addition, book reviews and other items of interest will be part of an annual, scholarly publication.

The present volume, coming to light in the year of transition is neither fish nor fowl. Three articles appearing here were not part of the workshop, but they are included because of their importance to our audience. Therefore, this publication is, shall we say, the last of the old, and a glimpse of the new.

The Workshop Articles

The theme of the Fifteenth Workshop for Bishops was *The Gospel of Life and the Vision of Health Care.* The keynote address was given by the Most Reverend Alfred C. Hughes, Bishop of Baton Rouge, Louisiana. As head of the bishops' Committee on Doctrine, he oversaw the drafting of the revised *Ethical and Religious Directives for Catholic Health Care Services.* He spoke about the process by which they achieved their final form and the tough issues the committee and its advisors had to confront in completing the revision.

Father Benedict Ashley, O.P., a frequent speaker in this forum, spoke on the documents of Catholic identity. He notes that today, it is necessary to understand clearly what the Church does and why she does it in light of the increasing secularization that is going on in society at large, and in light of the sensitive ecumenical situations opened to the Church's mission especially in light of the Second Vatican Council. "What is Catholic about Catholic health care?" is a question that will not go away.

Michael F. Collins, M.D., President of Caritas Christi Health Care Corporation and Secretary for Health Affairs to the Cabinet of the Archbishop of Boston, addressed the issue of the ethics of managed care. What are physicians becoming in the process of the evolution of health care delivery in the managed care setting? Dr. Collins spoke from his vast experience as both physician and administrator about the "two coats" he must wear: the white coat of the care giver and the blue coat of the business executive.

Thomas Murphy Goodwin, M.D., from the Division of Maternal-Fetal Medicine of the University of Southern California at Los Angeles, spoke of the clinical aspects of problem pregnancies. He discussed the ways physicians can resolve (and lay to rest) what seem to be insurmountable difficulties which will apparently result in the loss of life of either mother or child. It is a misunderstanding of these "conflicts" that mistakenly lead some to conclude to the "necessity" of abortion, even partial-birth abortion.

Monsignor James J. Mulligan of the Diocese of Allentown offered pastoral strategies for overcoming the culture of death. In contrasting current tragic events with the teaching of *Evangelium vitae*, Mulligan argues that "There is, in one sense, little or nothing that can be done to formulate the final strategy for overcoming a culture of death. At least that is the case if what we expect to find is the right law or the right argument or the right intellectual approach. The true solution lies elsewhere. The culture of death has to be overcome by replacing it with a true culture of life....[W]e cannot draw people to it with logical arguments alone." Authentic witness to the joyfulness of Christian faith is what is needed for a world in search of meaning.

Peter J. Cataldo, the Center's Director of Research, provides an update on the most recent developments in reproductive technologies and, with the aid of a metaphysical analysis, suggests definitions of terms and a criterion by which to evaluate the morality of specific procedures in light of the teaching of *Donum vitae*. He also provides a new defense of the morality of Gamete Intrafallopian Transfer (GIFT), subject to any magisterial determination on GIFT.

Joseph J. Piccione, J.D., corporate ethicist of the OSF Health Care System in Peoria, spoke of balancing justice, fiscal realities, and moral norms in the current state of the provision of health care. It is often claimed that in order for a hospital to survive–so that it can care for the poor–part of our moral teaching (generally the teaching on contraception) must be suspended. Piccione addresses the need to be consistently honest about what we believe and how we act as Catholic health care providers.

In my capacity as President of the Pope John Center, I have dealt extensively with health care institutional partnerships. I spoke on the principles of cooperation and their bearing on how to proceed in partnership initiatives. This continues the presentation I gave on this topic a year ago (published in last year's proceedings, *The Splendor of Truth and Health Care*). I also discuss "immediate material cooperation," "scandal" and "duress," all terms which are widely used, but never defined.

Helen Alvaré, Director of Planning in the Secretariat for Pro-Life Activities of the National Conference of Catholic Bishops, spoke of her experience with the Vatican delegation to the United

Nations conferences in Cairo, dealing with population and development, and in Beijing, dealing with women's issues. She addressed the "behind the headlines" aspects of political strategies. The Most Reverend James T. McHugh, Bishop of Camden and expert member of the same delegation, addressed the substantive issues of the conferences and the Church's concerns about them.

Additional Articles

Three additional articles appear in these pages. The first two originally appeared in the Italian publication *Medicina e morale*.

The Most Reverend Elio Sgreccia, Vice President of the Pontifical Academy for Life and Professor of Bioethics at the Catholic University of the Sacred Heart in Rome, writes about the innovative aspects in the presentation of the constant teaching of the Church on respect for human life displayed in *Evangelium vitae*.

From the same issue of *Medicina e morale*, we present an article by Professor Ignazio Carrasco de Paula, who writes about the consistency of the Church's teaching on respect for life and the alterations in its presentation by examining both *Donum vitae* (from the Congregation for the Doctrine of the Faith) and Pope John Paul II's encyclical *Evangelium vitae*.

Last but not least is an article by Father Brian Mullady, O.P., Professor of Systematic and Moral Theology at Holy Apostles' Seminary in Cromwell, Connecticut. Mullady's article is in response to an article by the Honorable John T. Noonan, "Development in Moral Doctrine," which appeared in *Theological Studies* (vol. 54, [1993], 662-677). It is Mullady's position that the changes in the practical conclusions about such issues as usury and marriage do not reflect a contradiction of previous dogmatic teaching.

*   *   *   *

The Pope John Center board members and staff would like to thank the many people who helped to bring about the Fifteenth Workshop and this publication. The Knights of Columbus once again made the Workshop possible by their generous grant. We are very grateful to all our benefactors.

We are also grateful to the workshop faculty who are so patient with the Center's deadlines. A word of thanks goes to the Most Reverend Charles V. Grahmann, Bishop of Dallas, to the seminarians of his diocese, who served at the Masses, and to Father Thomas Cloherty, who served as liturgical coordinator (and good friend), for their hospitality. We are grateful to the local councils of the Knights of Columbus and Catholic Women's Guilds of greater Dallas for all their work. Thanks goes also to our translation team in Dallas: Father Rutilio J. del Riego, Monsignor Monsignor Isidro Puente Ochoa, Ph.D., and Sister Margarita Cecilia Velez, O.P., and also to Sister M. Nieves, P.D.D.M., for her help in Boston. We must also thank the staff of the Harvey Hotel in Addison. We are very grateful to the Colettine Poor Clare Federation of Mary Immaculate for their prayers for the workshop's success. And finally, a word of profound gratitude to Daniel Maher, managing editor of this volume, Mrs. Jeanne Burke, and Mr. Donald Powers for their indefatigable work and apparently infinite patience.

The Reverend Russell E. Smith
Editor in Chief

Feast of St. Vincent de Paul, 1996
Emmitsburg, Maryland

To My Brother Bishops
Taking Part in the Fifteenth Workshop Organized by the Pope John XXIII Medical-Moral Research and Education Center

Again this year the Pope John XXIII Medical-Moral Research and Education Center has brought together a distinguished group of the Church's Pastors to examine the increasingly complicated issues of medicine and health care in the light of the patrimony of the Church's moral teaching. I gladly greet each one of you in the Lord Jesus Christ. I am confident that these days of study, reflection, and prayer will be beneficial to you in your role as shepherds and teachers of Christ's flock in North and Central America, the Carribbean, and the Philippines. I am once more very grateful to the Knights of Columbus for their generous support of this important gathering.

Your theme this year is "*The Gospel of Life* and the Vision of Health Care." As I wrote in my Encyclical *Evangelium vitae,* "The Gospel of life is at the heart of Jesus' message. Lovingly received day after day by the Church, it is to be preached with dauntless fidelity as 'good news' to the people of every age and culture" (no. 1). Indeed, "the Gospel of God's love for man, the Gospel of the dignity of the person and the Gospel of life are a single and indivisible Gospel" (no. 2).

The Gospel of life is more than ever necessary in our times. As we look back over the century which is now coming to a close, we see the emergence of an outlook and a way of life which in many cases takes the form of a veritable "culture of death." As Pastors of souls, you know full well that at the heart of the tragic growth of the culture of death there is *the eclipse of the sense of God and of man,* typical of secularism, which succeeds at times in penetrating and misleading Christian consciences. Moreover, a theoretical and practical atheism undermines people's capacity to appreciate human life in all its splendor and fullness.

Against this background, and in the exercise of the responsibility which is mine as Successor of Peter, I intended the Encyclical *Evangelium vitae* to reiterate in the strongest possible terms the sanctity of life and the intrinsic evil of the taking of innocent life (cf. no. 57), whether by abortion (cf. no. 62) or through euthanasia (cf. no. 65). I am confident that during your Workshop you will deepen your own perception of the foundations of this teaching, in order to communicate it ever more convincingly to the faithful entrusted to your ministry. It is important that everyone in the Church understand why Christians must fully assume "the inescapable responsibility of *choosing to be unconditionally pro-life*" (no. 28). Furthermore, the Pastors of the Church cannot fail to call Catholic Institutions to absolute respect for life, reminding them when necessary that "causing death" can never be considered a form of medical treatment, even when the intention is to comply with a patient's request (cf. no. 89).

Witness to the Gospel of life must be consistent and indivisible. It is very important that health care facilities staffed by Religious or connected to the Church in any way give faithful witness to the Gospel of life. Every aspect of Catholic health care must be permeated by the evangelical message of the redemptive meaning of the suffering and death, united to the Lord's Cross (cf. no. 88). Hospitals, clinics and convalescent homes should radiate that warmth, hope, compassion, and solidarity which are the best antidote to acts which are really a desperate travesty of "mercy."

As Bishops, we are the first ones called to be untiring preachers of the *Gospel of life*; we must hand it on in all its integrity; we must make sure that it is taught with conviction, especially in theological faculties, seminaries, and Catholic institutions; we must use appropriate means to defend the faithful from all teaching which is contrary to it (cf. no. 82).

May the Holy Spirit sustain and guide your efforts in this most important field. I commend your gathering to the intercession of the Blessed Virgin Mary, Mother of the Church, that you may proclaim the Gosple of life with honesty and love to the people of our time (cf. no. 105). With affection I impart my Apostolic Blessing.

From the Vatican, 11 January 1996.

Joannes Paulus PP. II

Greetings from the Knights of Columbus

Virgil C. Dechant
Supreme Knight

On behalf of the Knights of Columbus I am pleased to extend greetings to the Fifteenth Bishops' Workshop organized by the Pope John XXIII Center with the Knights' assistance.

The Knights of Columbus looks upon its involvement in these annual workshops to be a valuable way of offering support to the ministry of the Church's pastoral leadership. Our Order is pleased to have the opportunity to be part of the Dallas experience.

This year's workshop has, it seems to me, an especially timely theme: "The Gospel of Life and the Vision of Health Care."

It is good to know that, according to the program, the health care apostolate will be considered in light of such significant new documents of the Magisterium as Pope John Paul II's encyclical *Evangelium vitae* and the revised and updated *Ethical and Religious Directives* of the Bishops of the United States.

It seems clear that numerous complex questions confront Catholic health care institutions and Catholic health care providers today. Generally speaking, these questions are of two kinds.

First, there are questions regarding specific ethical and moral issues relating to the health field. In many cases, these are the result of scientific and technological advances, welcome in themselves, which in practice create new circumstances calling for careful discernment and prudent choice.

Second, there are new institutional challenges pertaining to the autonomy, the Catholic identity, and the religious and moral integrity of Catholic health care institutions and programs seeking to cope with changing patterns in the delivery of health services. I am happy to learn that many of these matters will be discussed during this year's workshop in Dallas.

The Knights of Columbus and its million and a half members—and their family members—have a real stake in your deliberations.

Many of our members and their family members are themselves directly engaged in the apostolate of Catholic health care. And virtually all of us, obviously, either are or soon enough will become health care consumers.

As committed Catholics, furthermore, we are proud of the witness to Gospel values that the Catholic health apostolate traditionally has offered to the world. We are anxious that this witness be maintained and strengthened in the years ahead.

Against this background, then, I offer good wishes to the bishops, speakers, and staff who have come together in Dallas for what promises to be a most fruitful event.

CHAPTER 1

A Catholic Vision of Health Care as Reflected in the *Ethical and Religious Directives for Catholic Health Care Services*

THE MOST REVEREND ALFRED C. HUGHES

Introduction

The purpose of this essay is not to address new issues or carve out new ground, but rather to provide a backdrop for the 1996 Workshop by offering some understanding of the *Ethical and Religious Directives for Catholic Health Care Services*, adopted by the National Conference of Catholic Bishops in the United States in November of 1994 and published in March of 1995.

Background for the Document

The original NCCB document, *Ethical and Religious Directives*, was published in 1971. This underwent a minor revision four years later. In 1987, the NCCB Administrative Committee appointed a special commission to determine whether the Conference should do a second revision. After wide consultation and study, this commission recommended in 1989 that a new edition be prepared

1

to take account of recent Church teaching and developments in medical science. The task was first assigned to a special commission and then assumed by the Committee on Doctrine. The text was submitted twice to the body of United States bishops for consultation and once to the Congregation for the Doctrine of the Faith. It was adopted by the United States bishops in November 1994.

It may be helpful to identify the significant reasons that led to a decision to revise the 1971 and 1975 documents. Many had come to realize that a coherent Catholic culture, both in the Church at large and in our Catholic health care institutions had disappeared. The mantle of leadership had passed from religious to laity. Medical staffs were composed not only of Catholics but also of many who were not. Even Catholic doctors and nurses had limited education and formation in Church teaching. Hence there emerged a desire on the part of many involved in health care to have an expanded document which would provide teaching as well as directives. Moreover, developments in medical science and technology (for example in reproductive technology, genetic testing for prenatal diagnosis, and intensive care technologies) raised the need for facing new questions. Magisterial teaching had already begun to address a number of issues not contained in the original document. Finally, changing economic and social contexts were exerting significant pressures on Catholic health care facilities and services.

Ethical and Religious Directives

General Introduction

The General Introduction to the *Ethical and Religious Directives* presents a theological basis for health care ministry from a Catholic perspective. It may be helpful to recognize some of the fundamental principles enunciated in this succinct presentation of the underlying theology for the Church's ministry in this area. As Catholics we have a firm faith conviction about the origin and destiny of the human person. Each person has a sacredness and a dignity that is due respect and support. The human person is composed of both body and soul. This is important in recognizing the responsibilities in health care, for Christian healing is related to the fullness of life. Jesus came to offer life and he promised to offer it abundantly (John 10:10). Suffering is a mystery. It is to be alleviated whenever possible. It is also to be embraced as profoundly redemptive when united with the suffering of Jesus Christ.

Part One

Part One of the document focuses on "The Social Responsibility of Catholic Health Care Services." This section locates the health care ministry within the wider context of the Church's social teaching. The expository treatment in this section enunciates fundamental principles: the sacredness of human life and respect for human dignity; the biblical mandate to care for the poor; the commitment to contribute to the common good; the responsibility to exercise good stewardship of available health care resources; the need to witness to objective moral standards in offering health care.

Then the directives focus on the distinctive nature of the Catholic health care service and the special responsibilities of both the local Church sponsoring the entity and the personnel engaged by the entity to fulfill this mission (1-9).[1] The directives encourage Christlike care and service (2) and call for an explicit commitment to offering health care to the poor (3). Each health care facility should exercise responsible stewardship for the good of the health care facility itself and also the wider community (6). Moreover, the Church engaged in health care is called upon to fulfill its own social teaching with regard to employment, termination, and compensation of employees (7).

Part Two

Part Two focuses on "The Pastoral and Spiritual Responsibility of Catholic Health Care." This responsibility flows from the very close relationship between body and soul in the human person. Those engaged in health care need to have a wholesome respect for human dignity, including the eternal destiny of each person. Hence, pastoral and spiritual care are integral to good health care.

The directives then call for the provision of appropriately trained personnel in pastoral care (10-11). They also provide guidelines for sacramental ministry in the health care setting (12-20). Finally, the directives clarify the role of the bishop in the explicit approval or confirmation of the appointment of priests and deacons and the development of a diocesan policy for the

[1] The numbers in parenthesis refer to the directives in *Ethical and Religious Directives for Catholic Health Care Services.*

engagement of appropriate ecumenical or interfaith personnel (21-22).

Part Three

Part Three of the *Directives* focuses on "The Professional-Patient Relationship." Both patient and professional participate actively in the healing process. Hence the relationship between professional and patient needs to be marked by mutual respect, trust, honesty, and appropriate confidentiality. When there is a team of providers, as is common today, this mutual engagement of professional and patient is even more important in order to preserve the human dignity and partnership with the patient. The professional and the patient should be helped to appreciate the moral and spiritual dimensions to full healing.

With this background the directives then focus on the need for respect for the inherent dignity of the human person by engaging the patient directly in the healing process (23). Any advance medical directives must be followed and respected in accordance with state law and fulfilled to the extent that they are consonant with Catholic teaching (24). Persons identified in advance as surrogates to make health care decisions must be respected and their decisions followed, also to the extent that they are consonant with Catholic teaching (25). Free and informed consent for medical treatments and procedures requires all reasonable information including risks, possible side effects, consequences, costs, and any reasonable alternatives to proposed treatments (26-28).

The right and duty to preserve bodily and functional integrity needs to be preserved. The donation and reception of transplanted organs are encouraged as long as essential bodily functions are not impaired and the anticipated benefit to the recipient is proportionate to the potential harm done to the donor (29-30).

Any medical experimentation must be done with the free and informed consent of the patient or the patient's surrogate. The greater the person's incompetency and vulnerability, the greater the reasons must be to perform medical experimentation (31). Ordinary means should be used to preserve health. Extraordinary means need not be adopted and must be evaluated in terms of the reasonable hope of benefits in contrast to any risks and burdens for the patient (32-33).

Patients have a right to privacy and confidentiality regarding information related to the diagnosis, treatment, and care they are receiving (34). Care for those who are victims of abuse or sexual assault is carefully spelled out (35-36). Ethics committees should be available to assist by advising in particular ethical situations, by offering educational opportunities, and by reviewing and recommending policies (37).

Part Four

Part Four then addresses "Issues in Care for the Beginning of Life." Respect for human life from its beginning extends to respect for the marital act by which human life is transmitted. Whenever possible and appropriate, there should be a commitment to prenatal and postnatal obstetric services for mothers and children. The directly intended termination of pregnancy (abortion) is intrinsically wrong. Prenatal diagnosis is permitted to provide preventive care for mother or pre- or postnatal care for the child, but never with the intention of aborting an unborn child with a serious defect. The promotion of responsible parenting through natural family planning efforts should be the centerpiece of the teaching and counseling with regard to family planning.

This teaching then leads to a series of important directives. The unitive and procreative ends of the marital act must be preserved. Hence, heterologous fertilization is always prohibited. Homologous fertilization is forbidden when the technique used leads to extra-corporeal conception (38-41). Participation in contracts for surrogate motherhood is not permitted (42). Adoption should be promoted as a morally acceptable and recommended alternative to abortion (43). The directly intended termination of pregnancy before viability or the directly intended destruction of a viable fetus is never permitted (45, 47-49). The physical, psychological, moral and spiritual care for persons who have suffered from the trauma of abortion should be provided (46).

Prenatal diagnosis is permitted when the procedure does not threaten the life or physical integrity of the unborn child or the mother and does not subject them to disproportionate risks. Direct sterilization of either men or women is not permitted in the Catholic health care institution. Procedures that induce sterility are permitted when their direct effect is the cure of a present pathological condition and a simpler treatment is not available (53). Genetic counseling may be provided in order to promote responsible parenthood and to prepare for the proper treatment and care of children with genetic defects in accordance with Catholic moral teaching (54).

Part Five

Part Five treats "Issues in Care for the Dying." Christ's redemptive grace enhances the whole person, especially in his or her illness, suffering, and death. There is a profound meaning to death. The destiny of the human person is eternal life. Support needs to be provided to both patient and family. Catholic health care services should embrace a commitment to ease the pain of a person who is dying. Euthanasia or physician-assisted suicide is never a legitimate means to alleviate suffering. The task of medicine is to care even when it cannot cure. The gifts of organs or bodily tissues are encouraged for ethically legitimate purposes.

This teaching then leads to the following directives. Patients need to have adequate information about the approaching reality of death and the legitimate choices available to them in providing either for medical treatment or for death (55). A person has a moral obligation to use ordinary or proportionate means of preserving his or her life, but may forgo extraordinary or disproportionate means (56-57). Nutrition or hydration should be provided to patients even by artificial means as long as this is of sufficient benefit to the patient to outweigh the burdens involved (58). The free and informed judgment made by a competent adult person concerning the use or withdrawal of life-sustaining procedures should be respected unless it is contrary to Catholic teaching (59). Euthanasia and medically assisted suicide are intrinsically wrong and cannot be tolerated (60). The patient should be kept as free of pain as possible. Medicines capable of alleviating or suppressing pain may be given to a dying person even if this therapy may indirectly shorten the person's life, so long as the intent is not to hasten death (61). Catholic health care institutions should not make use of human tissue obtained by direct abortions even for research or therapeutic purposes (65-66).

Part Six

Part Six of this document gives attention to "Forming New Partnerships with Health Care Organizations and Providers." In addressing joint ventures, Catholic health care institutions are asked to give preference to collaboration with health care systems and providers that share Catholic or similar values and ethical convictions. Any joint venture with a health care entity involved in activities that the Catholic Church judges morally wrong must be limited and governed by the principles of cooperation. Scandal, the leading of others into sin, must be avoided or rendered as remote as possible.

This teaching, then, provides the background for a series of directives. Decisions that may lead to serious consequences for the identity or reputation of Catholic health care services or entail a high risk of scandal should be made in consultation with the diocesan bishop or his health care liaison (67). The diocesan bishop must give his approval of joint ventures sponsored by institutions subject to his governing authority; he must grant a Nihil Obstat for such ventures sponsored by religious institutes of pontifical right (65).

Formal cooperation, in which the cooperator adopts the intention of the wrongdoer, is never acceptable; material cooperation, if rendered mediate so that the cooperator is distinguishable from the evildoer, can be tolerated for a proportionately serious reason (69). Cooperation that in all other respects is morally appropriate may be refused because of the scandal that would be caused in the circumstances (70).

Sources for the Teaching and Moral Guidance

The Ethical and Religious Directives for Catholic Health Care Services is rooted in the teaching of Scripture, the tradition of the Church, and natural law as recognized and interpreted within the Church. Thus, the document relies on Vatican II's *Gaudium et spes* and *Apostolicam actuositatem.*

In addition, these directives draw extensively from papal writings such as Pope John XXIII's *Mater et magistra,* Pope Paul VI's *Humanae vitae,* Pope John Paul II's *Solicitudo rei socialis, Salvifici doloris,* and *Veritatis splendor.* Moreover, Vatican documents, such as the *Declaration on Procured Abortion, Declaration on Euthanasia,* and *Instruction on Respect for Human Life in its Origin and on the Dignity of Procreation: Replies to Certain Questions of the Day,* provide guidance in some of the beginning and end of life issues. Finally, the NCCB's *Health and Health Care* and *Economic Justice for All* provide background for the introductory section.

The Most Neuralgic Issues

There were four principal neuralgic issues that surfaced in the course of the preparation of the document. Each of them

7

involved considerable research and consultation before the adoption of the final form of the teaching and the directives involved.

Sterilization. Some Catholic health care institutions had been expanding the interpretation of therapeutic sterilizations. Some Catholic bishops of the United States had been in conversation with the Congregation for the Doctrine of the Faith over this issue. In July 1993, the Congregation for the Doctrine of the Faith issued an official response entitled *Responses on Uterine Isolation and Related Matters.* Directive no. 53 of the document *Ethical and Religious Directives for Catholic Health Care Services* incorporates the response of the Congregation for the Doctrine of the Faith:

> Direct sterilization of either men or women, whether permanent or temporary, is not permitted in a Catholic health care institution when its sole immediate effect is to prevent conception. Procedures that induce sterility are permitted when their direct effect is the cure or alleviation of a present pathology and a simpler treatment is not available.

Ectopic pregnancies. The Committee on Doctrine was in direct consultation with the Congregation for the Doctrine of the Faith with regard to the wording of directive no. 48. The final wording was embraced with the guidance of the Congregation for the Doctrine of the Faith: "In case of extrauterine pregnancy, no intervention is morally licit which constitutes a direct abortion."

Artificial nutrition and hydration. The Committee on Doctrine had originally proposed to refer to the various statements expressed by state bishops' conferences in the United States. The Congregation for the Doctrine of the Faith asked that the statement of the NCCB Committee on Pro-Life Activities be given special prominence. Hence in the expository section, the following statement is made:

> Some state Catholic Conferences, individual bishops, and the NCCB Committee on Pro-Life Activities have addressed the moral issues concerning medically assisted hydration and nutrition. The bishops are guided by the Church's teaching forbidding euthanasia, which is "...an action or an omission which of itself or by intention causes death, in order that all suffering may in this way be eliminated."[2] These

[2] Congregation for the Doctrine of the Faith, *Declaration on Euthanasia,* May 5, 1980, Part II. Latin text: *Iura et bona, Acta Apostolicae Sedis* 72 (1980), 1542-1552.

statements agree that hydration and nutrition are not morally obligatory, either when they bring no comfort to a person who is imminently dying or when they cannot be assimilated by a person's body. The NCCB Committee on Pro-Life Activities report, in addition, points out the necessary distinctions between questions already resolved by the Magisterium and those requiring further reflection, as, for example, the morality of withdrawing medically assisted hydration and nutrition from a person who is in the condition which is recognized by a physician as the "persistent vegetative state" (PVS).

Directive 58 simply states: "There should be a presumption in favor of providing nutrition and hydration to all patients, including patients who require medically assisted nutrition and hydration, as long as this is of sufficient benefit to outweigh the burdens involved to the patient."

Forming new partnerships. The forming of new partnerships became a very difficult issue for the Committee on Doctrine to address since each proposed model for a partnership seemed to have so many unique features that it was difficult to develop universal norms. At one point the Committee proposed to present examples of partnerships. However, the Committee eventually determined that the best thing to do was to develop directives dealing with the role of the diocesan bishop in the decision-making process and then to indicate the need to follow the moral principles governing cooperation and scandal in the reaching of decisions regarding such joint efforts. In the Appendix a brief summary of the principles of cooperation is then presented.

Conclusion

The *Ethical and Religious Directives for Catholic Health Care Services* offers a vision of Catholic health care. They do not propose to be the last word. They are, however, a responsible statement of theological and pastoral principles, with seventy specific norms to guide concrete moral behavior in the providing of health care. The directives revolve around the sacred dignity of the human person and address both the social and personal morality of respect for the human person from the first moment of conception to the last natural breath. It is my hope that an overview of this document and its development will provide a helpful backdrop for the specific sessions of this 1996 Workshop.

CHAPTER 2

The Documents
of Catholic Identity

BENEDICT M. ASHLEY, O.P.

Catholic identity is in question for two reasons: (1) The existence of the Catholic community in today's pluralistic and relativistic culture demands that we know what distinguishes us from others; (2) The ecumenical and evangelical mission of the Church requires us to enter into dialogue with others. Hence, Catholics feel a great tension between remaining at the same time true to themselves yet open to others of very different convictions. This tension is especially acute in institutions that are sponsored by the Church yet are of service to the public, such as our schools and health care facilities.

The most authoritative of the documents of identity are unquestionably those of Vatican II and the *Catechism of the Catholic Church*—the first because it was an ecumenical council, the second because it was an effort engaging the entire college of the bishops to provide a unified statement of the Catholic tradition based on Vatican II along with the interpretation given to that council by the papal Magisterium in its many post-conciliar encyclicals, apostolic exhortations, and other instructions. By way of example as to how this conception of Catholic identity applies to Catholic-sponsored institutions we have the recently revised *Ethical and Religious Directives for Catholic Health Care Services.*

The council did not attempt to present a unified picture of what it is to be a Catholic, but produced a set of documents dealing with particular current problems. Yet as one rereads these documents they have a unity. First of all, *Dei verbum* (*Dogmatic Constitution on Divine Revelation*) establishes the source of the council's teaching and *Lumen gentium* (*Dogmatic Constitution on the Church*) expounds what God founded the Catholic Church to be and also what it is to be a member of that Church. *Sacrosanctum Concilium* (*Constitution on the Sacred Liturgy*) prescribes the renewal of the Church's ultimate act and supreme goal, the worship of God.

Second, certain sections of *Lumen gentium* were then expanded in the documents: *Christus Dominus* (*On the Pastoral Office of Bishops in the Church*); *Presbyterorum Ordinis* (*On the Ministry and Life of Priests*); *Optatum totius* (*On Priestly Formation*); *Perfectae caritatis* (*On the Renewal of Religious Life*); *Apostolicam actuositatem* (*On the Apostolate of the Laity*); *Gravissimum educationis* (*On Christian Education*), on its special care for youth.

Third, the council dealt with ecumenism and evangelization: *Unitatis redintegratio* (*On Ecumenism*); *Orientalium Ecclesiarum* (*On the Eastern Catholic Churches*); *Nostra aetate* (*On the Relation of the Church to Non-Christian Religions*); *Ad Gentes divinitus* (*On the Church's Missionary Activity*).

Fourth, the council faced precisely the issue of the tension between its own identity and the modern world in *Gaudium et spes* (*Constitution on the Church in the Modern World*), along with the central question that modernity has raised, the question of human freedom, in *Dignitatis humanae* (*On Religious Freedom*) and in particular in *Inter mirifica* (*On the Means of Social Communication*) with freedom of speech.

It has been this fourth area in which a polarization of the sense of Catholic identity has widened since the council, because the "progressive" wing of the Church has seen it as an invitation to mediate between the faith and culture by rethinking the whole tradition of the Church so as to free it of all that is not essential and thus enable it to assimilate as much of modern culture as possible. On the other hand, the "conservative" wing of the Church has seen *Gaudium et spes* as simply a repetition of the emphasis on family life and social justice found in the papal encyclicals, having little import for a rethinking of more doctrinal issues.

As a consequence of this polarization and the confusion it has caused in the transmission of the faith to post-conciliar generations, the bishops requested the writing of the *Catechism of the Catholic Church*, which can be regarded as an attempt to give a unified synthesis of the teachings of the council along with other elements of the tradition to which the council did not give special attention. Parts I and II of the *Catechism* detail God's self-revelation through creation, his word, the Incarnation, and the sacraments. Part I of the *Catechism* presents the Creed of the Church and its ecclesiology in a way that is more patristic than former neo-scholastic expositions, but which makes little reference to the post-conciliar theological revisionism. The thought of Rahner, Schillebeeckx, Küng, etc., has had little influence on Part I, but the researches of the patristic and more moderate biblical scholars have contributed much. Thus if the *Catechism* succeeds, the future identity of Catholics will rest firmly on a faith in a cosmos in which angels and devils are a reality, the Incarnation is understood as St. Basil and St. Augustine understood it, and the Church is hierarchical.

This creedal statement is complemented by Part II on the sacraments in which the post-Tridentine legalistic understanding has been replaced by a strongly patristic spiritual-realism that has assimilated much of the riches of Eastern mysticism. That type of liturgical fixism which wanted nothing changed in the liturgy has been replaced with a great emphasis on the dynamic action of Christ's Holy Spirit in the Church.

The other half of the *Catechism* deals with our response to God's self-revelation made possible by Christ's Holy Spirit.

Part III, the most thoroughly revised portion of the first draft, places the Commandments in the context of the New Law of Christ's Holy Spirit. Yet it firmly rejects the notion, which tended to dominate in the post-conciliar period, that this leads to an ethics of creative decision (proportionalism) rather than to the classical theology based on the finalities of human nature. This direction for Christian morality was even more firmly enforced by the encyclicals *Veritatis splendor* (*The Splendor of Truth*) and *Evangelium vitae* (*The Gospel of Life*). Moreover, the emphasis on social justice is very strong in Part III and has been reinforced by several papal social encyclicals and the instructions of the Congregation for the Doctrine of the Faith on liberation theology, which have pointed out that the Church's call to fulfill God's Kingdom "on earth as in heaven" does not mean socialism or any form of utopianism. Finally, Part IV, on spirituality, completes this instruction on the Christian life by showing Christians that they must live in the Spirit and under the guidance of the Spirit of Christ, not the spirit of the world.

From these documents it is clear that the Magisterium remains obedient to the council's call for church unity, a point recently underlined by the encyclical *Ut unum sint* (*That They May Be One*). In *Evangelii nuntiandi* (*Evangelization in the Modern World*) the Magisterium seeks to renew evangelization by finding formulations of the faith adapted to the plurality of world cultures and it continues its efforts for social justice. But at the same time, in line with the council, it is convinced that these goals cannot be achieved by changing its traditional dogmatic and moral positions.

This seeming doctrinal intransigence raises the question, so disturbing to the progressive wing of the Church: "If the Magisterium continues to 'retrench' and refuses to permit sufficient freedom of criticism and dissent from its traditional positions, how can it be possible for us to mediate between the gospel and culture in a rapidly changing, pluralistic world, especially the modern world, in which freedom of thought and discussion is seen as a fundamental human right?" Of course, conservatives will answer this objection by saying that the notion of "freedom" espoused by the modern world cannot apply to the *depositum fidei* to which Catholics must remain committed, since these truths are held not on the basis of human reasoning but on divine authority. To this the progressive can reply that the Church itself admits a "development of doctrine," a "hierarchy of truths," and "levels of authority of magisterial teaching." Consequently, it is dishonest and a disservice to the Church's mission to prevent freedom of discussion at least within these limits. Thus, cannot one, as progressives say, be a good Catholic and still dissent from at least some magisterial teaching?

The unequivocal answer of Vatican II, which has been reiterated by Paul VI, John Paul II, and the Congregation for the Doctrine of the Faith, is that dissent from magisterial teaching on dogma and morals is not possible for the loyal Catholic, who must give it at least "a religious submission of mind and will." After the council, some progressives, such as Hans Küng, attacked the very notion of infallibility. He argued that the human mind is inherently incapable of infallibility and wanted to substitute the notion of the indefectibility of the Church for its infallibility. Other progressives, like Charles Curran, argued that short of infallible declarations by the Magisterium, dissent is a right, and he and others extended this area of legitimately possible dissent to the whole of moral teaching since they questioned whether the councils or popes had ever solemnly defined moral norms.

The "retrenchment" of which progressives complain under John Paul II has consisted in reminding us that Vatican II explicitly obliged Catholics to magisterial teaching even when it was not infallible, and it did not limit the primary object of infallibility to the extraordinary exercise of the Magisterium, but included its ordinary exercise, provided it was universal. Furthermore, it left in place the traditional teaching that there is a secondary object of infallibility, namely, truths intimately connected with revealed truth, especially those whose denial is an equivalent to denying revealed truths. These latter are not the object of divine faith, since they are not directly revealed by God, but they are nevertheless irreformable. Thus, those who ask for the *Catechism* to label which teachings are infallible and which not might well be answered that there is very little in the *Catechism* that is not clearly part of the *depositum fidei* in the broad sense that it can never be essentially changed, although it may in the future be better formulated.

Is there, then, no room in the Catholic Church for a freedom of opinion that can open the way to necessary doctrinal development? First, even as regards solemnly defined dogmas, there is room for theologians to improve on the formulation and integration of these divinely revealed truths. Allow me to cite two examples only. For the sake of union with the Eastern Church we need a better formulation of the relation of the Holy Spirit to the Son, without, however, abandoning the dogma that the *filioque* was intended to express. Again, we need a more satisfactory way of speaking of the relation of the divine and human consciousness in Jesus, without, however, adopting a minimizing understanding of his personal divinity.

Second, as regards the vast area of dogmatic theology which is a mixture of biblical exegesis, sacred tradition, and theological opinion, we need a critical effort to develop theological positions that are consistent with modern scholarship while preserving the riches of Catholic tradition, without the distortion introduced by nominalistic and idealistic tendencies of modern philosophy and science apparent in too much of the post-conciliar speculative theology. The effort of Teilhard de Chardin to assimilate the theory of evolution failed because both his science and his philosophy lacked firm grounding. Again, in formulating eucharistic doctrine, the effort of Edward Schillebeeckx to substitute phenomenological "transfinalization" for scholastic "transubstantiation" proved a theological dead-end because of its idealism.

In the area of moral theology, the trend to proportionalism has proved a dead-end also, yet the Magisterium has left great areas of both personal and social ethical issues open to discussion. It has closed only those tendencies in sexual ethics which separate sexuality from the institution of the family, and in the area of politics certain theories that the experience of our own times have shown to be disastrous: individualism, totalitarianism, utopian anarchism.

Finally, in the realm of canon law, much of which is, of course, merely positive, the Magisterium has already made many reforms and is open to many more, provided that they do not reflect some ecclesiology inconsistent with that of *Lumen gentium.* For example, there is a wide opening for canonical changes that will permit much greater participation by women in the decision making of the Church, without undermining the divinely-instituted pastorship of the ordained hierarchy.

If, by way of example, we apply this conception of Catholic identity to Catholic health care services, the new revision of the *Ethical and Religious Directives* indicates clearly how this identity is to be maintained both negatively and positively. Negatively, a Catholic health care facility must not use intrinsically evil means, as these have been defined by magisterial instructions, some of which are common practices in today's culture (abortion, contraception, sterilization, reproduction in the laboratory, and euthanasia), on the mistaken view that these are pragmatically necessary ways of promoting human health.

The various efforts to justify these intrinsically evil practices in hardship cases or by a wrong application of the notion of material cooperation under duress has already gone far to erode Catholic identity in our health care facilities and medical education. We must strive to educate Catholic health care professionals to realize that these means are always wrong, not just because the Church

15

says so; rather, the Church says so because they are in truth not healing but harmful, and we should make sure that Catholic-sponsored institutions resolutely reject reliance on them.

Positively, the Catholic identity of such an institution is that those who control and enforce its policies are themselves faithful to magisterial guidance and attempt to educate their subordinates to follow the same standards intelligently and cooperatively. They must conceive their work above all as a ministry of the healing Christ whose heart goes out to the neglected, and they must carry out His ministry with a compassionate respect for their patients as human persons. Hence, they must subordinate to this mission their necessary concerns for its economic stability, its professional reputation, and its conformity to the cultural milieu. When seeming conflicts arise between the concern for the poor and the ethical limitations on the means that can be used, Catholics should remember that it is no real service to the poor to help them abort, contracept, sterilize themselves, or commit suicide.

When to do good by evil means is the only option our culture and our government seem to allow us, we should create new channels for our service to the poor, remembering the admonition of the Lord, If they will not hear you, "shake the dust from your feet" and go elsewhere (Luke 9:5).

CHAPTER 3

The Ethics of
Managed Care

MICHAEL F. COLLINS, M.D.

Introduction

In this presentation, I will discuss some of the many challenges confronting the Catholic health care ministry as a result of the tremendous increase of managed care throughout the United States. I was delighted to be asked to speak on the ethics of managed care, because since the introduction of antibiotics, there has not been a single influence that has had or will have a greater impact on the profession of medicine, and thus, our health care ministry.

I shall address this topic wearing two coats: the white coat of a medical professional and the blue suitcoat of a Catholic health care system administrator. I shall begin my presentation with a discussion of the basic elements of managed care and the influence they wield on the practice of medicine. Next, I shall focus on a great challenge that is facing health care as we approach the new millennium, namely the influence of profit motives in health care.

17

Lastly, I shall comment on the effect that managed care and profits will have on the future of our health care ministry.

These are complex questions. The responses to these challenges are similarly complex. Yet, I am pleased to have the opportunity to discuss the importance of our health care ministry, at the very moment that its survival as we know it is threatened. Through our actions and our commitment to the Catholic health care ministry, which has been passed into our hands through the example of Jesus,[1] we can continue as stewards of that ministry that is as essential to our Church today as it was in Jesus' time.

Before I take on these topics directly, let me speak of the Caritas Christi Health System of the Archdiocese of Boston, which I have the privilege to lead. Caritas Christi was created ten years ago through the vision and leadership of Cardinal Law. The principal purpose of Caritas Christi was and is to preserve *Catholic* health care so that the dignity of the human being and the primacy of human life could be foremost in the minds and actions of people caring for others.

Today, Caritas Christi is a comprehensive, integrated health system dedicated to caring for human life from the very moment of conception to the last moment of natural life. The System includes four acute care hospitals in Eastern Massachusetts, including St. Elizabeth's Medical Center of Boston, a major academic medical center affiliated with Tufts University School of Medicine.

In addition, in keeping with our commitment to provide a full continuum of care, we operate a center for pregnant and parenting teens, homeless women and their children, and victims of domestic or substance abuse, all located on the site of a former acute care obstetrical facility. We also operate a long-term care hospital, a hospice, a nursing home, and a home health agency.

Caritas Christi is a network of health care and service providers brought together first and foremost by a shared mission to *minister* to the sick and the needy. The fact that this ten-year-old integrated health care delivery network is the very model being replicated by the best minds in today's hospital world only affirms the strategic vision of Cardinal Law.

Simply stated, we are a ministry first and a health care business second. However, we *are* a business, and our ministry needs creative business strategies and solutions in order to succeed in a time of many challenges for the health care industry. So, let me

[1] Matthew 8:1-4, 8:14-17, 9:18-22, 9:27-31; Luke 4:40-41, 5:18-26.

put on my health care system administrator's blue suitcoat and discuss managed care and the potential of problematic ethical conflicts.

Basic Elements of Managed Care

First, what do we mean when we talk about managed care? On one hand, we have the conceptual managed health care model introduced over twenty-five years ago, in which the health care interests of patients, physicians, providers, and third-party payers are not only compatible but mutually reinforcing. As numerous billboards and radio ads inform us, this model promotes the primacy of the physician-patient relationship, it encourages the delivery of health care in the most appropriate low-cost setting, and emphasizes preventive and primary care. The physician is charged with managing the health care needs for his or her patient, the provider accepts with risk the responsibility to treat the patient in the most appropriate care setting, the insurer pays for the highest quality care at the lowest appropriate price, and the patient's health care needs are presumed to be fully served in an efficient, cost-effective manner.

Yet, the very essence of managed care is a reordering of control within the health care marketplace. Insuring entities which receive and distribute the health care premium are now in a position to manage the utilization of health care resources. Physician and provider entities are presumed to be the patient's advocate, but are clearly in a conflicted position, since their remuneration is directly impacted by the level of services utilized by their patient. Once a managed care entity is selected by a patient, a decision typically made when a patient is not ill, the patient's ability to access health care services and providers is limited by the managed care entity's network. Clearly, voice, choice, and access are managed.

A missing element in this potentially utopian alignment can best be described as the black hole of the control and profit motives, an unseen force, which in 1995 was responsible for sucking *hundreds of millions* of dollars out of the health care system. These were premium dollars paid by businesses and consumers but not used for health care services, or for free care, or to help educate physicians, or to discover new cures and treatments. These were dollars which were not returned in rebated or reduced premiums. These were *hundreds of millions* of dollars that the

19

HMOs and other payers kept for themselves as a return on investment or, in the case of for-profit insurers, paid out as dividends to shareholders.

The Influence of Profit Motives

The profit motive is the single most disruptive threat to the delivery of quality health care today. The reason that nearly 9 out of 10 acute care hospitals in the United States are organized as not-for-profit and tax-exempt entities is so they can focus *solely* on their mission of providing quality health care to the public. Managed care is controlling. Its incentives are not necessarily patient directed. Profits can be enormous as premium dollars are directed away from providers. Thus, we become faced with the central ethical issue.

Unlike other commodities, health care, whether it be in a fee-for-service or a managed care environment, should not be viewed solely as a product available for purchase.[2] As health care efforts are solely directed to the enhancement of human dignity, health care represents a good on which society places great value. To denigrate health care to a mere commodity is to diminish the value of the human person. To create an industry the entire purpose of which is to generate profits derived from treating people who are sick or in need of health care is to interpose between the patient and the care givers inherent disincentives to caring for the dignity of a fellow human and incentives to profit from another's misfortune.

Under a managed care insurance approach, we are asked to accept the supposition that "less is better." While reducing health care expenditures globally may, in fact, be a desirable societal goal, reducing expenditures for the individual patient may result in limiting desirable or appropriate services, leading to a decreased quality of life for the patient. Herein lies the ethical dilemma. While as a society we may be concerned about health care costs, as persons our concern for cost containment becomes diminished when *our* care is involved. As professionals, we strive to be patient advocates, caring first and foremost for the needs of our patients. As insurer representatives, a position to which we become relegated in a managed care world, care and quality may be our

---

[2] Cardinal Joseph Bernadin, "Making the Case for Not-for-Profit Healthcare" (A Speech at The Harvard Business School Club of Chicago, January 12, 1995).

motto, but our compensation or profits (managed care incentives) may cloud our judgment.

While efforts to improve efficiencies may expand the capacity of the delivery system to care for more patients, those efficiencies may result in physicians not spending adequate or appropriate time with patients, particularly in complex or unusual cases. I know that under some HMO models, physicians are expected to see a specific number of patients per hour. Their performance review and ultimately their salary is contingent upon their achieving that expectation. The ethical dilemmas in the day-to-day physician-patient relationship begin to emerge.

These ethical dilemmas result directly from the interposition of market and business forces between the patient and the care giver. This should be a concern to us all because, as managed care becomes increasingly prevalent in health care, all of us will be affected. As such, all of us should be concerned that the role and responsibility of our health care providers be clear and that their loyalties to our needs not be compromised by business practices or principles.

From my blue suitcoat perspective, let me share with you how our health care ministry is affected by the managed care world and review with you those elements which play an important role in it. I "affectionately" refer to them as the six Cs. They are: care, capitation, coverage, consolidation, conscience and, last but not least, Church.

Care

This essay is entitled "The Ethics of Managed Care." We must remember, while wearing our administrative blue suitcoat, that what sets excellent health care apart from mediocre health care is the *care*, not the *management*. What is important are the commitments inherent in the responsibilities of those who wear the white coat—at the bedside—those who provide personal, clinical care for the whole person. It is these moments of engagement between patient and care giver that are the hallmark of medicine as a profession and the distinctive element of our Catholic health care ministry: moments of personal care, free from the interruption and interpretation of business managers or others. I would argue this is particularly true for care provided at Catholic health institutions, which, I believe, attract staff and patients who place a higher premium on creating an environment that is committed to the art of caring. If the blue suitcoats of managed care are allowed to control the essence of the provider-patient relationship without the intervention of those of us who recognize the importance of caring in our health care ministry, then we are certain to see caring disappear as a lost art and the personal aspects of medicine driven out of the system or totally subordinated to business interests.

Capitation

Capitation is a method of payment for health services in which a provider is paid a fixed, per capita amount for each person served, without regard to the actual number or nature of services provided. In fact, no longer does the person maintain human dignity; they are subordinated to the position of a "covered life!" Think of a football stadium filled with one hundred thousand people. Let us assume that for each one of these people attending the game, a health care network will receive from an insurance company, one hundred and fifty dollars per month to provide for their health care needs throughout the year. That's right: care for the babies, the children, the parents, and the grandparents. Within such a large group, some will be sick and many will be well, but the payers of care will be in a position to share risk with the providers of care and perhaps even with the purchasers' agents, namely, the patients. No longer will care be the hallmark of the relationship. This shall be subordinated by a drive to control and reduce risk.

What are the implications of this risk sharing? From the Goodyear blimp high above the stadium crowd we see a seemingly healthy 18-year-old young man. On closer examination, however, it is revealed he is very sick with leukemia. Eighteen-year-old males are not supposed to be sick, they are not supposed to eat up capitated health dollars. Suddenly, the provider is expending sizable health resources on this patient's repeated hospitalizations and extensive home care. The young man gets sicker and sicker, his use of resources is extensive and continual. Suppose this patient becomes depressed and asks his provider, who was not expecting financially to care for this patient, to help him end his life. In a state with legalized physician-assisted suicide and a capitated managed care system, what is a provider to do? Imagine the dilemma! Do financial incentives and his patient's plaintive request blur the provider's professional judgment and deafen these words of the Hippocratic Oath:

> I will prescribe regimen for the good of my patients according to my ability and my judgment and never do harm

to anyone. To please no one will I prescribe a deadly drug, nor give advice which may cause his death.[3]

I do not believe that the principles of capitation are inherently unethical. Yes, the physician's concern must be and always remain the welfare of the patient and not the welfare of the managed care company. I will admit that there has always been an inherent conflict between the need for the patient to receive care and the need for the physician to receive a livelihood from the services provided to the patient. In fact, in a non-capitated system such as fee-for-service, the physician is reimbursed more for doing more for the patient. In that non-capitated system, there is no inherent disincentive to treat, in contrast to what might be created in a capitated system. Nevertheless, the physician's professional responsibility has been to do for the patient what the patient needs, as long as these needs are consistent with accepted medical practice and the conscience of the physician. When the physician's conscience and the patient's needs conflict, the physician's responsibility has been to make the necessary arrangements such that the patient's needs are fulfilled. But, it has been the *patient's* needs that have been the physician's prime concern. The professional relationship between patient and physician has not been encumbered by outside economic forces.

Coverage

As I stated earlier in my remarks, the responsibility as a society to provide coverage for all has not been well received by all. For the 85% of us with coverage,[4] we must try to imagine what it must be like to postpone seeking or to be denied health care because we do not have any or adequate health care coverage. Do we allow our children to play sports if we have no health insurance? Do we forgo career opportunities because a family member has a pre-existing condition which would be excluded by the new employer's insurance? As managed care is a phenomenon that does not presuppose health care coverage for all, but imposes the methods and limitations of its tenets on those with coverage, we can see the ethical dilemma inherent in a system where millions are uninsured and where providers are willing to manage care only for those with coverage. The responsibility of caring first (with

[3] Hippocratic Oath" as translated in *The Oxford Companion to Medicine*, 2 vols., ed. J. Walton, P. Beeson, R. Scott (New York: Oxford Univ. Press, 1986), p. 1747.
[4] 1993 National Health Interview Survey; National Center for Health Statistics.

which a not-for-profit system is imbued) could be supplanted by business and profit imperatives. Our commitment to universal access and universal coverage is seriously threatened.

Consolidation

Today, most communities are served by a community health care enterprise that has developed over the years. While we may not have a hospital in our own town, in most instances there is one not too far away with most of the services we need to preserve and to protect our health. Likewise, most of us have local access to physicians and other care givers through relationships we have chosen to establish and nourish. All of us recognize that the drive in our industry to consolidate is irrepressible and will surely impact our ability to seek care in the future from where and from whom we want. Managed care principles are concertedly and consistently limiting choice. As costs are being driven out of the system, so too are providers. Without universal coverage, continued consolidation will limit access, as not all patients will be welcome at the local provider's door. Not all providers will have the commitment or in some cases, the resources to care for all who are ill. Health care will become allocated as a scarce resource.

Consolidation is a market force that is occurring throughout the health care industry. Not unlike the forces that have affected banks and airlines, the consolidation and purchasing power, which is now centered in the managed care industry, is forcing provider entities to consolidate in an attempt to balance the control over access to managed care contracts. In many cases, this consolidation is purposeful and will result in a better use of community resources to serve patients. In many more instances, this consolidation threatens the very essence of community-based health care resources. It causes unnatural alliances and leads to consolidation decisions based solely on the pressure of the marketplace, the ego of the administration, and the force of the bond holder. Providers are consolidating without the needs and wishes of the patients and communities at the center of the effort. Catholic health care is not immune from these forces. Catholic identity is seriously challenged by the drive to consolidation. I shall return to this issue in a few moments.

Conscience

Conscience is an important consideration that will be impacted by the drive to managed care. The purchase of a managed care insurance policy often requires that services of a comprehensive nature be acquired and provided. This initiates a conflict between the purchaser and the provider from the perspective of conscience. As a purchaser, if my conscience requires that I not participate in certain medical procedures, am I required to pay for them even if I will never use them? As a provider, am I required to provide services I believe are wrong? In the case of an institution that contracts with managed care companies, if my institutional conscience dictates through a moral tradition that my institution not participate in certain procedures, will I be forced to provide them or will I be adversely affected in the contracting exercise because I refuse to participate? Again, these are not hypothetical challenges. Consider this story from the *St. Louis Post-Dispatch*:

> A new mandate [from the Accreditation Council for Graduate Medical Education] to provide training in abortion to prospective obstetrician-gynecologists has left some Missouri training programs in a quandary.
> For the two local Catholic programs, the question is how to preserve their accreditations without facilitating abortion, which the Catholic Church views as murder.
> For the University of Missouri at Columbia, the question is how to train students in abortions when state law bars spending public funds on the procedure.[5]

In matters of conscience, serious issues must be resolved in order to preserve the dignity of the person. If one's personal or institutional conscience becomes challenged by principles of business or compromised by disagreement, the fundamental freedom to participate in health care may be severely limited at great peril to person and profession alike.

Church

Finally, Church must also be considered as a market dynamic that could be severely affected by managed care. As the efficient, consolidated marketplace chooses to limit the number of providers and to contract with those entities that can provide full service, what will come of the Church-related entities that, because of conscience, may offer limited services in some areas and thus, could be excluded from large contracts, or that, because of a

[5] "Rule on Abortion Training is Perplexing," *St. Louis Post-Dispatch*, February 16, 1995.

commitment to caring, may provide extended services to the neediest or the sickest? While the Church's involvement in health care is of necessity big business, our Church has approached its ministry in health care as a calling from God. As such, the Church's actions in health care derive their imperative from the Gospel, which, one hopes, causes any financial considerations to be subordinated. Who will care for the uninsured AIDS patients or for pregnant and parenting homeless women? Who will minister to the dying elderly who are alone? If ministry is subordinated to business, who will do the caring? Can the moments of engagement be preserved?

The ministry of health care I have been speaking about has elegance in its simplicity. The business of health care is highly structured. Hospitals and other health care institutions in the vertically integrated structures that have been and will continue to be developed, are among the most complex social structures ever created. Myriad relationships exist in the health care industry where one finds highly structured bonds between for-profit and not-for-profit health care sponsors, providers, purchasers, consumers, and all the other constituencies that are directly affected by the business of health care.

The Effect of Managed Care and Profits on the Future

Another ethical dilemma posed by the increasing prevalence of managed care is the entrance of for-profit interests into the acute care marketplace.[6] This entrance and its rapid growth is easily understood when one recognizes the controlling influence on providers that is created in a heavily concentrated managed care marketplace. Secondly, access to capital is not guaranteed in the health care world. As margins are severely restricted, as contracting becomes more selective, as superstructure continues to be costly to maintain and as it continues to be necessary to adapt to changing infrastructure requirements (such as rapidly developing information technology and the need for physician business infrastructure support), the prevalence of managed care has caused a serious dilemma for those of us who come from the acute care, not-for-profit tradition and have Catholic identity. We must continue to maintain our patient-

[6] Cardinal Joseph Bernardin, *A Sign of Hope: A Pastoral Letter on Healthcare*, October 19, 1995.

centered commitment and gain access to capital, but now must do so in competition with entities that have profits as their primary objective and can raise capital in the for-profit marketplace. We must examine closely the impact of for-profit interests on the Catholic, acute care hospital and on our communities.

A definition of the word *profit* is, "financial or monetary gain obtained from the use of capital in a transaction or series of transactions."[7] The primary purpose of a for-profit enterprise is to earn a growing profit and to assure a reasonable rate of return on equity for the individuals who have created it and invested in it.

Hospitals are charitable institutions that are created to care for the needy, aged, infirm, or young. The fundamental purpose of not-for-profit hospitals is the non-economic goal of caring for the individual patient and promoting the person's human dignity—both charitable causes.

Where does the economic goal of earning a profit collide with the non-economic goal of caring for the needy, the aged, and the infirm? I would like to continue to say, "Not in Catholic health care," because I believe that Catholic, acute care hospitals have produced, pure and simple, the best, most caring hospitals in the country. Given our legacy of excellence in patient care,[8] service to our communities, medical education, and cutting edge research, we should move very carefully before embracing a for-profit, acute care model that necessarily challenges the fundamental tenets of our Catholic health care ministry.

Catholic health care is a service, a ministry. It is not a commodity to be bought and sold. Those who practice medicine, or run our nonprofit institutions, including the thousands of women religious, think of themselves as healers and service-providers, educators and researchers, professionals with a vocation, not as merchants and commodities brokers. The for-profit model of hospitals treats health care as a commodity to be bought and sold at the highest margin to the widest audience. Nothing could be or should be further from the motivation of Catholic health care institutions.

As I said, our legacy of caring rests on certain fundamental tenets. What are those tenets?

First and foremost is a relationship of trust and caring for our patients and the communities we serve. Our hospitals were

[7] *Webster's New World Dictionary,* Third College Edition (Simon & Schuster: 1988).
[8] See Christopher J. Kaufman, *Ministry and Meaning: A Religious History of Catholic Health Care in the United States* (New York: Crossroad, 1995).

founded as charitable institutions to serve our neighbors and our communities. The primary interest and obligation of the Catholic hospital always relates to, "What is best for the patient for whom we are caring? What is best for the community we serve?"

The primary interest and obligation in the for-profit world always relates to the commitment to ensure a reasonable return to shareholders. That is one of the dramatic differences in decision making in the for-profit and not-for-profit worlds. It is manifest in the dynamics of the board room: paid directors versus volunteer community leaders; return on equity and profits versus community needs and benefits; individual shareholder incentives versus patient care incentives.

Second, who is charged with the decision making at a not-for-profit hospital? The answer lies in the community of volunteers who serve on the institution's Board of Trustees. They are the neighbors of the patients who are served, they are the business leaders who care about their local hospital, they are the physicians who care for people in the hospital and in the community. And they are the patients themselves. They are motivated by a greater good, not by a greater return on shareholder equity.

How does decision making occur in the publicly traded for-profit model? There, the decision makers are ultimately the shareholders. They are not, in large part, from the community. They generally do not have a long-term interest in the institution or its community, and in the end, are motivated primarily by improving the return on their investment. When revenues are squeezed tightly, they must in turn squeeze down hard on services in order to sustain high shareholder returns. What they buy today, they may sell tomorrow to realize more profit! Their perspective, often from a thousand miles away, focuses on the next quarter's results and is not related to patient care or community benefit.

Health care in the investor-owned company is viewed as a commodity, not a good, that by its nature cannot be a mere commodity. Investor-focused incentives are fundamentally different from patient- and community-focused incentives.

In contrast, *our* not-for-profit status causes us to focus our business activities squarely on the charitable, health care service to which we are committed. Yes, we are big business but *our* primary interest is caring with a patient-centered focus. And as the business of health care evolves, we too must adapt to the market forces that are upon us. If managed care continues its penetration into the insurance market, and it will, if capitation becomes the primary payment mode, and it will, and if government support for health care, research, and medical education continues to decrease, and sadly I am afraid, it will, then we must continue to become more efficient and businesslike in the management of our health care institutions. But at the end of the day, the decisions made by the leaders of Catholic health care, many of whom are here today, must apply patient-first values to the practice and business of health care.

As for-profit hospital companies grow, their shareholders, hoping to increase the return on their investment, may cause them to diversify into unrelated businesses. These unrelated businesses may produce a better return for investors, thereby calling into question the economic advisability of the less profitable for-profit hospital activity. Or they may produce an economic loss for investors, thereby jeopardizing the ongoing, profitable hospital activity. Either way, the profit motive drives the decisions about our community's hospital services!

Simply stated, the for-profit incentives do not and can not put patients and their communities first!

Third, Catholic hospitals have passed the test of time. Nobody who has survived the changes in the health care marketplace for the past ten years has done so without facing up to the cold economic realities of the nineties. All of us are now in a sense regulated by the insurers and HMOs that monitor the cost of medical care. Within our own institutions, cost controls and decisions about the affordability of personnel affect every workday. All of our economic decisions are based upon providing the best quality of care for the patient. We begin and end by deciding what is best for the patient. In a for-profit hospital, the bottom line is a primary concern.

Fourth, given all the health care competition that exists even among Catholic hospitals, there still remains a commitment to the ministry fostered by our Catholic beliefs.

Will this spirit of cooperation and collegiality and this tradition of caring for the patient survive in a model where profits are a primary consideration? Will the for-profit entity have the freedom to do what is best for the patient if, as a primary concern, it has to worry about what is best for the investor? I think not.

As a patient, I worry that the risks and benefits of a particular procedure in my personal care might be weighed against an impersonal investor's potential profits or losses.

As a physician, I truly believe it is an expectation and an absolute privilege to care for patients and not to be expected to care only for the privileged.

As a Catholic, I am troubled that for-profit marketplace pressures and temptations will cause us to evolve from the position as stewards of strong Catholic hospitals, which are committed to a clear, Catholic identity, to less clearly identified hospitals in the Catholic tradition.

Today we have a once in a lifetime opportunity to reaffirm the greatness and the goodness of Catholic health care.

We have a value judgment to make. These decisions should not rise and fall solely on the business plans that are developed and the proformas that are envisioned. Such plans should not be developed as a response to intimidation from a managed care dominated marketplace. As a community of people, we must continue to value as our primary concern the people and community for which we care. I do not believe that it is possible to be both for-profit and Catholic. In the acute care hospital, one cannot serve both the need to return equity to the shareholders and to care primarily for a patient's human dignity. These dual and dueling primary incentives are not compatible. Joint ventures with for-profit interests should be carefully considered and not undertaken lightly. I do not believe that it is in the best interest of a Catholic entity to be in a joint venture with a for-profit entity. Our Catholic health care tradition is value-driven, not profit-driven. This tradition must be preserved.

However, I would challenge us today to assess whether or not we are prepared to preserve the central beliefs of our health care ministry as outlined in the recently-promulgated *Ethical and Religious Directives for Catholic Health Care Services* (1995). Will the pressures of managed care cause us to weaken our resolve and commitment to Catholic identity?

I would observe that the challenges faced by our ministry do not meet a consistent response from diocese to diocese, from sponsoring congregation to sponsoring congregation. Clearly, there is an inconsistency in the interpretation of and adherence to the *Ethical and Religious Directives*, particularly with regard to asset mergers, the development of networks, and the establishment of joint ventures. Why is this, when we have such a thoughtful document and a body of teaching upon which to make such decisions?

I would suggest that we must recognize that our ministry imperative is more important than the business imperative that heavily influences some Catholic health care decisions. Our ministry can be preserved despite intense business pressures if we remain committed to our Catholic identity and if we choose to partner with other Catholic entities as a way of facing the intense business pressures and forces of consolidation that exist in the marketplace. These decisions are complex. The challenges which face sponsors of Catholic health care institutions are real. Yet, we should not so often look to non-Catholic institutions as our potential partners before we have fully explored collaboration amongst Catholic entities. We should not continue to be so willing to accept compromise solely for the purpose of getting a deal consummated, when knowingly we compromise our Catholic identity in the exercise. We are a ministry that has survived many threats throughout the years and we are a Church rooted in values and principles. These values and principles must guide our actions.

Those of us in Catholic health care respond to Jesus' example and call to minister to the sick, the poor, and the infirm.[9] Being involved in Catholic health care today is especially exciting and humbling. We have the opportunity to demonstrate, powerfully, our religious and ethical commitments and in doing so, to influence the healing profession, and society as a whole.

The rationalizing of health care and the impact of managed care is forcing affiliations of health care corporations, facilities, professional services, and health care purchasers. What happens to the mission of Church-related institutions when market consolidations place them in a competitive position with other Church-related facilities or affiliations? Caring is not a competitive exercise. It is solely a human emotion. Caring has no business imperative.

This was brought home for me this past year when I had an opportunity to spend time with a colleague and contemporary of mine, who recently died from cancer.

He shared with me his own very disappointing experience as a managed care consumer. For two months, his persistent cough and low grade fever was treated by a nurse practitioner who served as the gatekeeper to his primary care physician, who in turn serves as the gatekeeper to the world of specialists and sub-specialists.

[9] Mark 8:1-4, Matthew 9:18-22, and 27-31.

Frustrated by his inability to see *his* doctor in a timely fashion, he circumvented the system and he was able to access world-class care in Boston teaching hospitals, in part because of who he was—a smart, savvy, health care consumer—and in part because he was lucky enough to live in the midst of a medical mecca.

However, the most compelling aspect of my friend's observation of our health care system was not a fixation on its failures and shortcomings, but his heightened appreciation of those moments of engagement of which I have been speaking. Moments of engagement with his care givers elevated and inspired him.

A gentle exchange about kids and family with a young internist who wrote him a moving "thinking of you" note. The tender squeeze of a hand from a technician helping him through a diagnostic procedure. The intimate sharing by a world-renowned researcher of his own personal experience with cancer.

My friend marked the days of his treatments by these moments. He was not simply a DRG to be treated and billed; he was not solely a capitated life; he was not only my friend. Most important, he was a person, filled with human dignity, who was sick, and who needed care. These moments of engagement and caring are white coat moments. They are grounded in the primacy of the relationship between care giver and patient and they are threatened by the blue business coat approach to medicine.[10]

If we in Catholic health care have one ethical tenet to uphold in the tumult of marketplace and government health care reform, it is our responsibility to ensure that the physician-patient relationship is preserved, and that meaningful moments of engagement in the delivery of care are protected and promoted. We must be vigilant in guarding against *any* health care reform that does not recognize the difference between the blue coat and the white coat.

There are no inherent ethical inconsistencies in managed care. Managed care has not one human quality. Any ethical inconsistencies shall be due to persons, be they health professionals or business executives. Persons who allow their incentives to become unaligned; persons who forget about caring; persons who become mesmerized by capitation; persons who become consumed by consolidation; persons who deny the

---

[10] Kenneth B. Schwartz, "A Patient's Story," *Boston Globe Magazine,* July 16, 1995.

imperative of universal coverage; persons who compromise with their conscience; persons who deny the importance of Church.

But there is hope! There are many more persons who are committed professionals. Committed to caring, challenged by capitation and consolidation, but committed to universal coverage, their conscience, their Church. But most important, compelled to moments of engagement with their patients in the example so poignantly given to us all by Jesus.

CHAPTER 4

Medical and Ethical Considerations Regarding Early Induction of Labor

T. MURPHY GOODWIN, M.D.

Introduction

Inducing labor prior to the estimated time of complete fetal maturity (37 weeks of gestation or 21 days from the "due date") is common in obstetric practice. Ending pregnancy by inducing labor may be medically indicated for the benefit of mother or child or both in the following circumstances: (1) preterm premature rupture of membranes; (2) various maternal medical complications, such as preeclampsia; or (3) evidence that the fetus is being harmed by staying *in utero*. When any of these conditions arises after *viability*–the point in gestation at which neonatal survival is possible (currently around 23 weeks gestation, provided proper perinatal facilities)–there is little ethical controversy about the practice of early induction of labor, as long as there is no disproportionate risk of injury to the child or to the mother. When, however, any of these conditions arises before viability, inducing labor can be expected to lead to the death of the child. Additionally, some fetal anomalies, such as anencephaly, are so

34

severe that the child has virtually no chance of survival beyond the neonatal period whether the pregnancy is allowed to proceed to term or labor is induced early. These cases, where inducing labor is indicated although the child cannot be expected to survive after birth, raise serious ethical questions both in the clinical setting and on the policy level for Catholic health care institutions.

This essay will review several categories of clinical settings in which there are medical indications for inducing labor although this would result in the certain death of the fetus or neonate or significantly shorten its lifespan.

1. Preterm premature rupture of membranes prior to viability
2. Herniation through the cervix of the intact bag of waters prior to viability
3. Preeclampsia prior to viability
4. Severe fetal anomalies that are directly lethal, such as anencephaly, or lethal without extremely aggressive intervention, such as trisomy 18 and 13

Following the consideration of these four categories is a case study of one pregnancy where complications were diagnosed near the critical time of viability. Consideration of this case will give some insight into the complexity of treatment decisions as they occur in the clinical setting.

Preterm Premature Rupture of Membranes
Prior to the Time of Neonatal Viability

If the chorionic and amnionic membranes rupture when the fetus has attained at least 18 but less than 23 weeks gestation, the chance of the fetus's eventual survival is small, but measurable. In most cases, rupture of membranes is followed by labor within a short period of time. If labor does not begin spontaneously, the principal risk of expectant management is ascending infection from the vagina into the membranes and whatever amniotic fluid remains around the fetus. Infection in these membranes, chorioamnionitis, could lead to systemic maternal infection, which can be life threatening. It is also unlikely that the newborn could survive without major handicaps. For these reasons, most non-Catholic hospitals offer the option of inducing labor despite the lethal consequences for the fetus. As gestational age approaches the critical time of viability, the patient and physician are more likely to opt for expectant management, usually with administration of antibiotics, and possibly steroids to enhance fetal maturity. However, practice remains highly variable.

Catholic moral teaching limits the acceptability of inducing labor following the preterm premature rupture of membranes. After the rupture but in the absence of chorioamnionitis inducing labor is direct abortion as defined in the *Ethical and Religious Directives for Catholic Health Care Services*:

> Abortion (that is, the directly intended termination of pregnancy before viability or the directly intended destruction of a viable fetus) is never permitted. Every procedure whose sole immediate effect is the termination of pregnancy before viability is an abortion....[1]

The rupture of the membranes does not of itself constitute a life-threatening pathology; terminating the pregnancy by inducing labor is therefore a direct abortion. By contrast, with the advent of chorioamnionitis a life-threatening infection is present. Procedures taken to protect the mother's life from this infection, including induction of labor, can be directly therapeutic even if fetal death is among the consequences of these procedures. This is also stated in the *Ethical and Religious Directives*:

> Operations, treatments, and medications that have as their direct purpose the cure of a proportionately serious pathological condition of a pregnant woman are permitted when they cannot be safely postponed until the unborn child is viable, even if they will result in the death of the unborn child. (47)

The mere rupture of membranes, without infection, is not serious enough to sanction interventions that will lead to the death of the child. Chorioamnionitis endangers the life of the mother and therefore constitutes a "proportionately serious pathological condition." Hence, in Catholic facilities, preterm premature rupture of membranes calls for expectant management, unless or until chorioamnionitis supervenes. In this situation, there is virtually no chance of fetal survival and, because the mother's life is in danger, induction of labor may be morally justified under the conditions stated above in directive 47.

[1] National Conference of Catholic Bishops, *Ethical and Religious Directives for Catholic Health Care Services*, approved November 1994 (Washington, D.C.: United States Catholic Conference, 1995), directive no. 45. (Hereafter reference to the *Directives* will be made by number in the body of the article.)

Permitting the induction of labor before viability in the presence of chorioamnionitis may be explained by appeal to the principle of the double effect. The conditions of this principle are as follows: (1) the act performed is in itself morally good or at least indifferent; (2) the good effect is directly intended and the bad effect is foreseen but unintended; (3) the good effect is not achieved by means of the bad effect; (4) the good effect is proportionate to the bad effect; (5) the good effect can only be achieved concomitant with, but not by means of, the bad effect. Consider the application of the conditions of this principle to the case of chorioamnionitis:

> The act in this case is the induced expulsion of pathological tissues from the uterus. Because the tissues are infected, this action is therapeutic for the mother and thus good, satisfying the first condition. However, labor also expels the non-viable fetus. Inducing labor or any similar treatment can be permitted, despite the ensuing death of the fetus, provided that the remaining conditions of the principle also are satisfied. The direct intention of the physician and the mother must be treatment of the chorioamnionitis, not termination of the pregnancy (2). The cure of the infection must not be achieved by means of the death of the child (3). The life of the child cannot be endangered by physician intervention unless the mother's life is endangered by the chorioamnionitis, not just the possibility of chorioamnionitis. That is, a pathology must be present, whose consequences for the mother are proportionately serious to the intervention's consequences for the child (4). Finally, labor may be induced only if the infection cannot be cured in some other way that would not result in the death of the fetus (5).[2]

Because of the lethal consequences of inducing labor prior to viability, the diagnosis of chorioamnionitis should be established unequivocally.

Herniation of the Intact Bag of Waters through the Cervix

The condition of incompetent cervix may allow the amniotic sac to herniate through the cervix, without any evidence of labor.

[2] Adapted from Peter J. Cataldo, "The Principle of the Double Effect," *Ethics & Medics*, vol. 20, no. 3 (March 1995), 1-3.

Under these circumstances, the physician may perform an emergency cerclage: replacing the bag in the uterine cavity and suturing the cervix closed. The bag of waters may rupture during this procedure, yielding the situation described in the previous section of this essay, namely, preterm premature rupture of membranes. Alternatively, the bag may not rupture, but the physician may be unable to replace it, in which case the prognosis for fetal survival is poor unless the pregnancy is already very close to viability. In either situation, i.e., if the bag ruptures during cerclage or if it cannot be replaced, many practitioners would strongly recommend inducing labor. Indeed, many practitioners will offer the mother the option of inducing labor without even attempting emergency cerclage, if it appears that cerclage would be technically difficult with a high likelihood of rupture of membranes.

Under any of these circumstances, it should be clear that inducing labor would constitute direct abortion in the moral sense. If, however, there is evidence of life-threatening infection, the induction of labor could become a method of eliminating the infected membranes, in accordance with the argument presented in the preceding section.

Severe Maternal Medical Complications: Preeclampsia

Preeclampsia is fundamentally a disease of the placenta.[3] Although the ultimate cause of preeclampsia is unknown, it is known that some agent produced by the placenta causes the hypertension and end-organ destruction in the mother which is characteristic of this disease. Preeclampsia occurring prior to viability is virtually always associated with an underlying maternal disease, usually of the vasculature or the kidneys. Accurate diagnosis of preeclampsia superimposed on the underlying condition can be difficult.

In cases of preeclampsia, induction of labor prior to viability could be justified by appeal to the principle of the double effect. Because the placenta is diseased, the immediate object of inducing labor is to remove the offending organ. The unintended but foreseen bad effect is the death of the child. All of the conditions

---

[3] *Williams Obstetrics*, 19th ed., F. Gary Cunningham, *et al.* (Norwalk, CT: Appleton & Lange, 1993), 767.

of the principle of the double effect stated above must also apply in this case.

Severe Fetal Malformation

In the case of severe fetal anomalies, induction of labor prior to viability simply because the child suffers some defect is a direct abortion. After the fetus has attained at least 23 weeks gestation, determining the moral significance of inducing labor is more difficult. The question usually arises in cases of severe anomalies that are either lethal of themselves (death anticipated in the neonatal period–e.g., anencephaly, renal agenesis, and certain skeletal dysplasias) or lethal in the absence of very aggressive intervention (e.g., trisomy 18 and 13). Extreme care must be taken to insure the accuracy of the diagnosis.

When the physician is confident of the accuracy of the diagnosis, he or she must examine the most recent information on the natural history of the condition and any possible therapeutic interventions. In some cases there will be no therapeutic options and the child can be expected to die at birth or shortly thereafter. Inducing labor will not alter the outcome; it will shorten the child's life by some few weeks or months. In cases where aggressive interventions may increase the chance of survival, preterm induction may reduce the already small chance of fetal survival even further.

For the moral evaluation of inducing labor under these circumstances, we start from the premise that it is appropriate to the dignity of all humans to live to the natural terminus of life. The importance of emphasizing this point to the couple who have just learned of their child's grave condition is, I believe, often underestimated. The child, no matter how gravely malformed, is to be shown respect and acknowledged as a member of the human family; one way we do this is by applying the same ethical principles we apply when dealing with all other persons. Oftentimes the clinical setting, where the initial diagnosis and discussion of prognosis occurs, in a sense strips the child of its attributes–intelligence, physical beauty, the ability to interact, all the expectations for the future. But the child is still a human being, made in the image and likeness of God. And by applying the ethical principles common to all humans we are not heartless, but compassionate.

The process of deliberation on the ethical aspects of such cases can ennoble the family and restore to them their child as someone for whom they are providing the best care they can in this decision. By contrast, the alternative of abortion says to the mother, in effect, "Your child is not part of the family of humans who are treated equally, but is somehow less, a kind of thing that can be set aside without the full acknowledgement that all humans require." Abortion, especially for the family that would not have otherwise considered it, often fails to bring the prompt resolution of the suffering that the abruptness and finality of the procedure itself seems to promise. Much the same may be said of routine early induction after viability.

Maternal-Fetal Interaction in Ethical Decision Making

In order to apply common ethical principles to decisions about early induction, we must understand the unique and complex nature of the maternal-fetal interaction. First, while decisions about therapy based on the benefit and burden to the mother change only with the course of the disease, such decisions for the fetus change constantly with advancing gestational age. All decisions about induction of labor must take into account that the fetal "benefit and burden" considerations are constantly changing from the point of viability up to term.

Second, neither the fetus nor the mother should be treated entirely independent of the other. In addition to the usual posing of risk versus benefit, the mother must ask: "Are the risks to my baby proportionate to the benefits I receive?" At the same time, the fetus (through its advocate) asks: "Are the risks to my mother proportionate to the benefits I receive?" Although the child cannot ask for its own annihilation, it can decline, as it were, treatment intended to prolong its life if the benefit of the prolonged life is outweighed by the burden on itself or on its mother. Just how natural and "taken for granted" this mutual consideration is can be seen in the exceptional cases where a mother, or more rarely, a fetal advocate decides about therapy without regard to the other.

In cases where continuation of the pregnancy poses any substantive risk to the mother, prompt induction of labor (or delivery by Caeserean section, as appropriate) is usually the best way to preserve maternal health. When delivery is delayed in spite of a substantive maternal risk, this delay of delivery becomes an active medical intervention on behalf of the fetus. This is readily perceived in obstetric practice where strategies for delaying delivery for fetal benefit (as in the case of preeclampsia early in gestation) are described as "aggressive." Delaying delivery for fetal benefit in the face of maternal risk is a *specific fetal treatment strategy*.

Through a surrogate the child *in utero* may evaluate this "treatment strategy" as to whether it offers a reasonable hope of benefit or poses excessive burden on itself or on its mother. Speaking with patients who face these difficult decisions, I find that the image of this continual dialogue between the child and the mother is not only comforting but serves as a firm touchstone for the ethical decision-making process.

The Meaning of "Viability" in Ethical Decisions

Such reasoning could be said to allow for the possibility of abortion, since the child *in utero* with a lethal anomaly could be said to benefit little from simply remaining alive *in utero* for the next four to five months. This benefit could be considered so small as to allow for the possibility that any burden on the mother would outweigh it, leading to a decision to end the pregnancy. To understand why this cannot be so we must understand the meaning of the term "viability."

The term "viability" is relative in the sense that the exact gestational age to which it refers depends on the services available at the time of delivery. For a given child in a given clinical setting with its available resources, there is a gestational age below which there is no reasonable expectation of survival. Hence, for the purposes of making ethical decisions, viability is the threshold at which the fetus is no longer dependent on the maternal environment to such a degree that delivery of the fetus would be synonymous with the death of the fetus or newborn. The fetus is viable when it has achieved a degree of physical maturity sufficient to survive. "Viability" is meaningful also for a gravely malformed child, even though the actual clinical judgment of the neonatal team who attend the child after birth may be to limit specific life-prolonging interventions. For example, diaphragmatic hernia is a particular malformation that reduces survival after very preterm birth to almost zero. Such a child may not survive long after delivery, but this will be due to its malformity, not directly due to delivery.

Even though a child with a serious anomaly may not make use of all the tools available at birth or not use them for long, these are available. This is seen in the way that, in most tertiary perinatal centers, the neonatal resuscitation team attends all deliveries to see how the baby responds to efforts in the first few moments of life. The postnatal decision as to what measures will be used is independent–guided in the main by principles of "reasonable hope of recovery" and "excessive burden."

The Case of Anencephaly

Anencephaly is one type of fetal anomaly for which some have recommended early induction of labor. In this condition, the covering skull bones (calvarium) are missing and the underlying brain is largely absent. In such cases there is, for all intents and purposes, no chance of survival beyond the neonatal period and no chance of higher brain function. Most physicians advocate abortion if the diagnosis is made early in pregnancy. If the diagnosis is made later in gestation, early induction of labor is often advocated. As mentioned above, even in Catholic institutions, early induction has been proposed as a humane option.

In justification of early induction, one rationale that has been offered is that there is no benefit to the fetus to continue to term since it will almost certainly die shortly after birth and, in any case, will never have any awareness of its family or surroundings. But, as we have set out above, the dialogue about early induction of a viable fetus must always begin with the mother's condition. If there is no substantive risk to the mother's health, then it is appropriate to the child *in utero*, no matter how malformed, to continue to the natural terminus of its existence. If some tangible risk from continuing the pregnancy does develop for the mother, the the anencephalic fetus, through its surrogate, could evaluate the "treatment strategy" of delaying delivery much as an end-stage terminal cancer patient might evaluate further chemotherapy. The aggressive treatment strategy of delaying delivery could be refused since the proportionate benefit to the fetus of living a few more weeks is outweighed by almost any substantive burden on the mother and the family.

One of the most difficult aspects of such a decision is the question of whether an emotional burden constitutes a substantive risk or burden. In fact, this is the maternal burden that is most often invoked to justify early induction of labor in cases of anencephaly, because there is rarely any physical risk to the mother arising from continuing an anencephalic gestation, whereas there is some risk arising from early induction. Directive 49 of the *Ethical and*

Religious Directives is not helpful in this regard since it does not make it clear whether emotional burden in and of itself qualifies as a proportionate reason. The directive reads: "For a proportionate reason, labor may be induced after the fetus is viable."

In assessing the emotional burden, the expected grief response must be distinguished from the much less common clinical depression. The latter can represent a substantive risk to the mother. In the absence of this, however, it can be argued that the only reason to induce is to hasten the death of the child for the purpose of ending the parents' grief. But to hasten the death of the child, either as an end or a means, is never permissible. It is crucial to the parents' understanding to remind them continually that the dignity of the child demands careful application of the principles proper to every member of the human family. To induce labor in order to shorten their emotional suffering is to declare that this child is less than fully human. Sadly, the longed-for resolution of the emotional suffering may actually be put off by the failure to acknowledge and accept the child fully, despite its defects.

Case Study

A 35 year-old mother of five in her sixth pregnancy was found to have increased amniotic fluid volume (polyhydramnios) and clenched hands at 22 weeks gestation. This suggested trisomy 18, a diagnosis confirmed by amniocentesis. The mother was presented with the option of pregnancy termination and the genetic counselor told her, "We will respect whatever decision you arrive at, but we have never had anyone who did not opt for abortion in recent years." Nevertheless, the mother refused abortion.

Subsequent counseling was directed towards a thorough understanding of the natural history of trisomy 18 and the postnatal prognosis. This involved detailing exactly which organs were involved and to what extent. An important finding was that the heart was unaffected since complex heart defects usually result in death early in the neonatal period, unless surgery is undertaken. The stomach "bubble" was absent in the child, a condition that suggests esophageal atresia. This was significant since a gastrostomy tube for feeding the infant and some sort of palliative procedure to prevent aspiration of oral contents would be necessary to prevent death from starvation or lung infection.

The couple learned that in the best case scenario, 5-10% of trisomy 18 children could live one year and 1-3% could live for five years, but that this figure was much lower for males (their baby was a male). Also, the figures mentioned above did not apply to babies with the specific defect of esophageal atresia, which their child was thought to have. The parents wondered if placing a gastrostomy tube after birth to feed their baby would be excessively burdensome. What about surgery to bypass the possible esophageal obstruction?

As the pregnancy progressed, emotional and physical burdens increased. The continued accumulation of excess amniotic fluid resulted in a uterine size twice that of a normal pregnancy at the same gestation. It was difficult to perform household duties and the mother's frequent emotional letdowns affected the entire family.

By 32 weeks gestation, the mother experienced intermittent difficulty breathing due to the size of the uterus and the mother felt "at her wits' end." The decision-making process was framed in terms of the benefit to the baby versus the burden on the baby and on the family. What is the proportional benefit to the baby of simply living at least another 5 weeks *in utero*? To what extent should the emotional burden on the mother be factored into this decision? To what extent should the psychological burden on the rest of the family be factored in? How important is the burden on the family of the mother's being unable to fulfill her role around the house?

The framework for approaching these questions was similar to that applied in all early induction decisions: with each passing day, the benefit to the baby of delaying delivery was less and, therefore, correspondingly smaller burdens on the mother and family might be considered sufficient to justify early induction of labor. In this specific circumstance, it was felt that inducing labor at 32 weeks reduced the child's chance of surviving longer than a few months without burdensome intervention to less than 1%, as compared to 5% for a child delivered after 37 weeks gestation. This was especially so if intubation and mechanical ventilation were viewed as burdensome intervention. There did not appear to be any tangible medical risks at the time. The principal burden at the time was the distress of the parents. This was not considered sufficient to justify delivery.

Based on these considerations, labor was not induced. One week later, however, when the mother developed significant respiratory difficulty, a decision was made to induce delivery. This was justifiable given the goal of preserving the lives of mother and child to the extent possible under the circumstances. Consideration was given to amniocentesis or other approaches to reduce the amniotic fluid volume, but it was felt that the risk to the mother was not justified by the slight benefit to the child. As Paul Ramsey has pointed out, weighing all the factors that pertain in such a complex decision requires, above all, a pure heart.

CHAPTER 5

Pastoral Strategies for Overcoming the Culture of Death

THE REVEREND MONSIGNOR JAMES J. MULLIGAN

What Does It Have To Do With Us?

In early 1995, near Allentown, Pennsylvania, a boy of 11 was cruelly killed along with his parents. The mother was stabbed and the father and son beaten to death. But that was not the only horror. It was revealed that the crime had been committed by the couple's two oldest sons. A few days later they were apprehended in Michigan. They confessed to the police and were sent home to stand trial.

The two boys were in their teens, and would have drawn attention, even if they had not been charged with murder. One look at them would have turned most people away. Their heads were shaved and their scalps tattooed with swastikas and the word "berserker." Both their crime and their appearance clearly set them apart from the comfortable world around them. They were a pair of outcasts. They were far from the norm – so far, in fact, that they could be taken for frightening curiosities with little or nothing to teach us about ourselves.

The local newspaper, the *Allentown Morning Call*, carried the whole story–right up to their guilty plea and life sentences. Reporters tried to understand how it had happened. Editorials bemoaned the sad state of society. And, when all was said and done, little had changed and the sad facts remained.[1]

In that same *Morning Call*, just a few years ago, there was a series of articles dealing with the sad plight of couples who desperately wanted to have children and were unable to. Fertility experts were interviewed, as were couples who have been either successful or unsuccessful in their attempts to become parents.

Anyone familiar with fertility treatments knows that many of them have drawbacks. Apart from the fact that treatment so often does not work at all, there is the worse problem that it sometimes works entirely *too* well. Too many children are conceived and cannot all live in the same uterus with any hope of survival. Doctors, therefore, sometimes practice what is referred to as "selective reduction" or "selective termination" or even "selective maintenance of pregnancy." (That last phrase especially has such a positive sound to it.) The fact is that all of them mean the same thing: Since not all of the conceived children can survive, some of them will be killed so that the rest can live. In these articles, two doctors were interviewed.

The first doctor said: "Ethically, I think it is very difficult to justify. Medically, maybe you can justify it because if you keep all of them, they may not make it, so let's just keep two, but ethically, which two are you going to keep? That really disturbs me."[2] The other doctor said: "It's the ethics of what is known as the common good. You have an individual tragedy for the betterment of the common good. In this case, that means a baby may have to give up its life so its brothers and sisters can live."[3] No matter how innocuous it is made to sound, it still comes down to the same thing: Some children are going to be purposely killed.

The first of the two doctors has obvious qualms about the whole thing. The second makes it sound almost heroic. Of course, he omits the fact that *it was he who put the innocent victims into this position in the first place.* He does not point out that these unborn

---

[1] See articles and editorials appearing in the *Allentown (Pa.) Morning Call* between early 1995 and the beginning of 1996.

[2] Dr. Sze-Ya Yeh, quoted in the *Allentown Morning Call,* July 30, 1989, p. B20.

[3] Dr. Gregory Lang, ibid.

children are totally *involuntary* "heroes." It is as if Adolf Eichmann had said that he admired the heroism of those who were gassed so that the healthier could live and be productive in the labor camps. We may rightly deplore all of this, but does it have anything to teach us about ourselves?

One final example. This same *Morning Call* a few years ago ran a cartoon that, perhaps more than almost anything else, brings out the contradictory nature of policies that are so widely accepted in our society. It was the picture of a woman, woebegone and clearly pregnant. She stood in a back alley amid garbage cans and squalor. A grinning doctor with a bloody apron and filthy hands looked out his open door and beckoned her in. In the caption she was saying, "The pro-life people sent me." This particular paper, of course, is consistently pro-abortion, and limits the extent of its morality to making sure that children are murdered in clean and sanitary conditions. A dreadful outlook, but has it anything to teach us about ourselves?

This paper rightly denounces murder, violence, and the destruction of families. It then hails the wonders of fertility treatments, even when they kill children or treat them as salable commodities. It proclaims the basic constitutional right of a mother to kill her own child before it can take its first breath. It praises the cleanliness of the abortion mills which cater to murder on demand. It reserves its most scathing ridicule for those who want to save life at its weakest. Yet, with all that this may say about the world in which we live, does it have anything to say about ourselves?

I have not focused on the *Allentown Morning Call* because I think that it is unique in what it does. In fact, it is not. It is really just a small town newspaper with wire service connections to the rest of the world. It is owned by the *Los Angeles Times* and, I would presume, follows a basic editorial policy set by its owner. It is an editorial policy not much different than that of the *New York Times*, *Philadelphia Inquirer*, *Washington Post*, *Boston Globe*, or *Baltimore Sun*.

I am sure that every one of those publishers, if asked, would lay claim to being in service of the betterment of life, and yet every one of them is caught up in a culture of death. Every one of them makes the same assumptions: Legality and morality are the same thing; we have the right to do anything to further our own happiness; death is better than suffering; life is ours to do with what we will. All of this leads to a kind of practical advice which, when we look clearly at it, is not only wrong and sinful, but simply stupid: Protect animals, but don't hesitate to kill the unborn; outlaw the use of animal parts in experiments, but legalize the use of aborted babies instead; don't discourage abortion, just make sure it is done in a nice, clean room. Simplify the corporal works of mercy: Don't visit the sick and bury the dead, bury them both instead. In this whole outlook there is nothing that gives life, but a great deal that causes death. And what, we might ask, does all of this have to do with us?

Evangelium vitae

It has, indeed, a great deal to do with us. This world in which we live is *our* world, given to *us* by God. It is in this world that we are to work out our salvation and come to share in the life of God Himself. It is this world that has its influence on us and to which we attempt to extend God's grace. This was clearly in the mind of Pope John Paul II as he wrote his encyclical, *Evangelium vitae*, and pointed to the stark contrast between the "culture of life" and the "culture of death."[4]

There is a moral indecisiveness that is part of the society in which we live. Absolutes are held in distrust. This results in a lessening of subjective responsibility, but it also creates a situation in which everything is affected by a *"structure of sin"* (*EV*, 12). Members of this society become increasingly inclined to find their own self-centered and self-satisfying solutions to the problems of life. That will inevitably lead to a preoccupation with the sort of efficiency that creates a *"war of the powerful against the weak"* (*EV*, 12). The most devastating result of this attitude is described with vivid clarity by the Pope. He says:

> [A] life which would require greater acceptance, love and care is considered useless, or held to be an intolerable burden, and is therefore rejected in one way or another. A person who, because of illness, handicap or, more simply, just by existing, compromises the well-being or life-style of those who are more favored tends to be looked upon as an enemy to be resisted or eliminated. In this way a kind of *"conspiracy against life"* is unleashed. This conspiracy involves

[4] The terms *culture of life* and *culture of death* are used time and again in *Evangelium vitae* (March 25, 1995). *Culture of life* appears in sections 21, 28, 50, 77, 82, 86, 92, 95, 98, and 100, and *culture of death* in 12, 19, 21, 24, 26, 28, 50, 64, 87, 95, and 100. (Hereafter this encyclical will be cited in the body of the text as *EV* with section numbers).

not only individuals in their personal, family or group relationships, but goes far beyond, to the point of damaging and distorting, at the international level, relations between peoples and States. (*EV*, 12)

Our culture takes subjectivity to an extreme. It "recognizes as a subject of rights only the person who enjoys full or at least incipient autonomy and who emerges from a state of total dependence on others" (*EV*, 19). This is humorous when all it means is that the only people who can get a bank loan are those who can prove that they do not need one. There is nothing humorous at all when it is the plight of those who are caught in poverty, weakness, or dependence, and so will not be heard when they plead for their own lives. The fact is that they *can* communicate, but *society does not want to listen*, because they "can only communicate through the silent language of a profound sharing of affection" (*EV*, 19) and that is a language that selfishness cannot understand. There is a profound contradiction at the heart of a society that makes the most solemn affirmations of human rights, and then simply denies them in practice to those too weak to secure them for themselves.

It is even sadder to realize that the worst sorts of neglect or rejection are disguised as altruism. Abortion and euthanasia are presented as solutions to human problems rather than as the tragedies they really are. Freedom is treated as isolated autonomy, and completely loses its relational dimension. What is really being lost here? The Pope expresses it perfectly when he speaks of "the heart of the tragedy being experienced by modern man: *the eclipse of the sense of God and of man,* typical of a social and cultural climate dominated by secularism" (*EV*, 21). The loss of the sense of God results in the loss of the understanding of the source of human life and dignity.

When we speak of the eclipse of the sense of God and man, what does that imply? It implies the loss of both the *bond* between God and man and the *distinction* between God and man. It implies that in some way man usurps the place of God. It implies the loss of the objective foundation of all moral choice. Right and wrong become not objective realities, but simply a matter of individual choice. Human conscience is not treated as *recognizing* an objective distinction between right and wrong, but as though it *creates* right and wrong. The saddest result of this is a deplorable confusion between good and evil, right and wrong (*EV*, 24).

We experience this not only in the obvious moral conflicts of our culture, but in ways more subtle. Ways that seem not so significant, and yet, perhaps, can teach us even more about ourselves. Look, for example, at the things that are taken for granted in entertainment. Words, ideas, plots that would never have found their way into public view a few decades ago and are now taken for granted on prime time television. Even worse, perhaps, are the things we may find ourselves laughing at. We are constantly faced with ridicule of the Church, ridicule of Catholic education, ridicule of motherhood, ridicule of family life. We are encouraged to deride what we once held sacred. We laugh at what should make us sad. We act ashamed of what should be a source of pride. We begin to apologize for what we should proclaim as the truth.

Pope John Paul II writes: "When conscience, this bright lamp of the soul (cf. *Mt* 6:22-23), calls 'evil good and good evil' (*Is* 5:20), it is already on the path to the most alarming corruption and the darkest moral blindness" (*EV*, 24). This is, perhaps, the real blasphemy against the Holy Spirit, that unforgivable sin.[5] It is the failure to attribute to the Holy Spirit those things which can come only from the Holy Spirit. To confuse good with evil and so run the risk of never even recognizing the need for forgiveness. "The one who will not accept the work of the Spirit has made it impossible for himself to recognize the word and the work of God. Only he can be forgiven who confesses that he has something to be forgiven."[6]

This may sound much like the network news, with its delight in doom and gloom. If there is a shortage of new tragedies on a given day, the news falls back on the seasonal ones. Every August we hear of the unbearable heat and the dire droughts—which, of course, occur every year and which always lead to the autumn rains. It is like having daily reports of the onset of night, while avoiding all mention of the fact that darkness will then be followed by dawn. The truth is that things are *not* all doom and gloom. There are wonderful people all around us. There are married couples who love each other, who rejoice in their children, and who make enormous sacrifices to hand on the gift of God that they have received. There are families willing to accept homeless,

[5] In *The Jerome Biblical Commentary*, ed. Raymond E. Brown (Englewood Cliffs, N.J.: Prentice-Hall, 1968) see John L. McKenzie, S.J., "The Gospel According to Matthew," p. 85 (43:83), Edward J. Mally, S.J., "The Gosepel According to Mark," p. 29 (42:23), and Carroll Stuhlmueller, C.P., "The Gospel According to Luke," p. 146 (44:109).

[6] Ibid., J. McKenzie, "The Gospel According to Matthew," p. 85 (43:83).

abandoned, or handicapped children. There are volunteers who willingly spend themselves to share the graces of a loving God. There are all about us signs of the unity of God and man (*EV*, 26).

But there is, at the same time, the constant clash between the culture of death and the culture of life. Tremendous value is placed on pleasure and well being—so much so, that any serious sort of "suffering seems like an unbearable setback" (*EV*, 64). The result is that just when you might expect every effort to be made to preserve life, instead death is offered as the solution to all of life's real problems.

> Death is considered "senseless" if it suddenly interrupts a life still open to a future of new and interesting experiences. But it becomes a "rightful liberation" once life is held to be no longer meaningful because it is filled with pain and inexorably doomed to even greater suffering. (*EV*, 64)

This may make no sense at all, unless we realize that it stems from a fundamental failure to accept our relationship with God. It happens because man thinks of himself as his own rule and measure, "with the right to demand that society should guarantee him the ways and means of deciding what to do with his life in full and complete autonomy" (*EV*, 64). And so a society that proclaims the value of life is willing to kill the unborn when they become burdensome to the enjoyment of life. A society that seeks cures for all ills, turns to euthanasia when life becomes too painful. There is no meaning in life itself once all value is placed in its pleasures instead, and no goal beyond this life is recognized.

Saint Paul's Epistle to the Romans

There is, in one sense, little or nothing that can be done to formulate the final strategy for overcoming a culture of death. At least that is the case if what we expect to find is the right law or the right argument or the right intellectual approach. The true solution lies elsewhere. The culture of death has to be overcome by replacing it with a true culture of life. Our whole Catholic Christian tradition of life in Christ is already such a culture. The fact is, however, that we cannot draw people to it with logical arguments alone. We can only do so by *living* the reality of the gospel of life that we preach. The real strategy of overcoming the culture of death means *living* in a new way, not merely arguing in a new way or legislating in a new way.

It would be foolish to think that the intellectual truth of the matter is not important. It is very important–but something further is demanded. We must look into the deepest needs of humanity. These needs are totally real, and yet are sometimes not recognized for what they are even though they are felt by each of us. They are needs that cry out for fulfillment, and then, sadly, we seek that fulfillment in the wrong place. This has been the case from the beginning and is constantly being addressed in the Scriptures.

Saint Paul's letter to the Romans was written to a culture in many ways no different than our own. The Christians of Rome knew from experience what it was to live in a "culture of death." One book on daily life in ancient Rome begins with the following statement:

> The birth of a Roman was not merely a biological fact. Infants came into the world, or at any rate were received into society, only as the head of the family willed. Contraception, abortion, the exposure of freeborn infants, and infanticide of slaves' children were common and perfectly legal practices. They would not meet with disapproval or be declared illegal until a new morality had taken hold....[7]

In such a society there was no innate or inalienable "right" to life. There was merely a "privilege" granted by society or family until the individual became old enough and strong enough to make his own demands and enforce them. This is precisely how our culture treats the unborn.

Two of the most popular and influential philosophies of Paul's time were Epicureanism and Stoicism. Even though Christians were more attracted to Stoicism than to Epicureanism, both philosophies found suicide acceptable. The same book on ancient Rome's private life says this:

> The Stoics believed that human beings feel innate affection for their families and cities, so that if duties toward these are neglected, feelings of incompleteness and unhappiness result. The Epicureans, on the other hand, held that human

[7] Paul Veyne, ed., *From Pagan Rome to Byzantium*, trans. Arthur Goldhammer, vol. 1 of *A History of Private Life* (Cambridge, Mass.: The Belknap Press of Harvard University Press, 1987), 9.

happiness requires us to abide by only those pacts that we ourselves have ratified out of deliberate, self-interested calculation. Both sects held that a man who, because of illness or persecution, found it impossible to lead a humane life in his body or his city would reasonably resort to suicide; indeed, suicide was the recommended remedy in such situations.[8]

Both the Stoics and the Epicureans looked only within themselves for their ideals, for their happiness and for the meaning of life. Both philosophies fell short of the mark and concluded that in time of deepest need there was no answer except to end it all. It is the perfect example of a culture of death. And so too are certain trends in our own time.

Both philosophies lacked any moral basis outside of man himself. Christianity was different and came as a breath of fresh air to the Roman world—and so it may come to our own age as well. Yet we and the Christians of first-century Rome, share a common contradiction. We, as well as they, live in a society that lays claim to high ideals and then answers the problems of life with death.

When Paul wrote to the Christians of Rome in 58 A.D., he was well aware that they lived in a society filled with pagan cynicism and an over-exaggerated sense of self-reliance. They rejected or just simply ignored the relevance of their gods. Yet it remained a society that *spoke* of its gods and carried out its religious practices as *civic and social functions*—a culture uncomfortably like our own! That may be hard for us to accept, because our society is ostensibly religious and even likes to call itself Christian. But it is too often evident that religion does not succeed in getting beneath the surface, and that proclaiming oneself Christian is no guarantee of the living of Christian life.

Paul's letter to the Romans looks at something absolutely basic. It is this: When we live apart from God and his grace, we go nowhere. He looks at the Jews who had received the Law from God and who had fallen into the trap of thinking that they now saved themselves by their own keeping of the Law. He looks at the pagans who had lost sight of God entirely, and whose own experience was forcing them to see how futile was their life without God.

It would be a mistake to think that what Paul is saying here is something like this: "If we do not keep God's law, we will be

8 Ibid., 224.

punished. God's wrath will come upon us and we will feel pain and destruction." The fact is that he is saying something much sadder and much more frightening. He is saying this: "Over and over again man has rejected God and refused to see him. Finally, in order to bring man to his senses, God gave him what he wanted. He let him become a law unto himself." Paul says that he "abandoned them with their heart's cravings, to impurity, and let them degrade their own bodies."[9] This is the real terror: God has not been vindictive or wrathful. He has simply given us what we want and it has been found a horror.

Man worshiped what was not God, and so came under the dominion of what is less than God—less even than man himself. The creative power of his own sexuality—a power reflective of the God whom he should have seen as Creator—was distorted, and sex became selfish pleasure rather than life-giving creativity. Man, now left to himself, became enslaved to his own selfishness and turned to murder, fighting, gossip, slander—the whole catalogue of vices that Paul sees as emerging from the ignoring of God by man and the subsequent and truly dreadful ignoring of man by God. The punishment is all the more horrible because it does not come from God; it pours out of man himself. Paul says that, perhaps worst of all, "they know God's decree that those who act in this way deserve to die, yet they not only do it, but applaud any who do."[10] They teach people to laugh at what is right and best, and to seek satisfaction in what is worst. Sin becomes self-perpetuating, self-justifying and drags others along in its wake.

Paul then speaks of the Jews, but in a different way. He says something that we should apply immediately to ourselves. They knew that idolatry was wrong and they knew that the vices of the pagans were truly vices. They bore proudly the sign of their circumcision, a sign that separated them from the pagans. But circumcision will help *only if it is the outward sign of an inner reality.*[11] "The real Jew is the man who is one inwardly, and real circumcision is a matter of the heart, a spiritual, not a literal, thing. Such a man receives his praise not from men, but from God."[12] We

---

[9] Rom. 1:24. All scriptural quotations in the text and notes, unless otherwise noted, are taken from *The Bible: An American Translation,* J. M. Powis Smith and Edgar J. Goodspeed, (Chicago: The University of Chicago Press, 1963).

[10] Rom. 1:32.

[11] "Circumcision will help you only if you observe the Law; but if you are a law-breaker, you might as well be uncircumcised" (Rom. 2:25).

[12] Rom. 2:29. The phrase translated as "circumcision is a matter of the heart, a spiritual, not a literal thing," is *peritomē kardias en pneumati ou grammati,* i.e., "circumcision of the heart in spirit not in letter."

deceive ourselves if we think that the external trappings of religion mean anything without the true, internal transformation that each day renews our hearts.

Paul is clear that what saves us is not our own self-sufficiency in keeping the Law, but the grace of God to which we respond in faith. Our act of faith is not just a simple human action. That would imply just one more rule, as though the Law demanded that we have faith, and we therefore decided to do it. Rather, the faith must involve some internal reality, some internal transformation, by reason of which God's promise comes to life in us. If we are looking for a strategy for overcoming the culture of death, then this is where it should really begin. We must allow God into our lives, and allow his presence to make us into a new creation. We must not keep God at a distance, and so force him to abandon us to our own devices. This also means that our preaching should maintain its focus on transforming hearts, and not simply on changing minds.

Saint Paul is also well aware of something else that our modern culture seems to have lost. That is the truth of the reality of sin. Both sin and salvation imply a solidarity of the individual with the race.[13] "Through one man sin came into the world, and death followed sin, and so death spread to all men, because all men sinned."[14] Paul draws a clear parallel between the effects of Adam's sin and Christ's redemptive act. The necessity of salvation arises from the results of Adam's sin on all men and from the effects of the personal sins committed by everyone, Jew and gentile.

> As one offense meant condemnation for all men, just so one righteous act means acquittal and life for all men. For just as that one man's disobedience made the mass of mankind sinners, so this one's obedience will make the mass of them upright.[15]

Sin involves both the solidarity of the human race and acts freely chosen by individuals.

Saint Paul calls us to look at the reality of redemption by looking first at the implications of the reality of sin. Redemption is no mere matter of an act of Christ performed to make up for an otherwise inevitable punishment. It is not simply a matter of an act of obedience that sets an example for our future obedience. It is a

---

[13] Cf. Rom. 5:12-20.
[14] Rom. 5:12.
[15] Rom. 5:18-19.

question, rather, of realities deep within the core of our being. Paul J. Achtemeier, in commenting on the fifth chapter of Romans, points to a notion which is at the heart of a real understanding of the distinction between a culture of death and a culture of life. He says that there are two possible fates for humanity—sin leading to death and grace leading to life. He writes:

> The problem of physical death as the result of sin is a major problem…for the modern person. The reason lies in the fact that we are simply not accustomed to thinking of sin as a power capable of altering the structure of reality. Seeing death as the result of sin points to the profound effects of sin— in Genesis 3 Adam's rebellion affects even the productivity of the soil (Gen 3:17-19). To an age trained to think of "sins" as moral peccadillos, this dimension of sin will seem all but incomprehensible. Yet reflecting seriously on it will help us understand the seriousness of sin. God's Son hardly needed to die to alter the effects of moral slips. Paul is involved here in a discussion of the ontological aspect of sin (i.e., its power to alter reality)….Whether or not Paul speculated on Adam's possible immortality prior to the Fall, it is clear his understanding of the effects of human sin included repercussions far beyond the deleterious effect on personal life and human society. For Paul, those effects reach all the way to an adverse effect on the very structure of reality.[16]

This is something else that we need to learn. Sin is deadly. It is not just an infraction deserving punishment. Sin is destructive. It is a deadly trap to see it as no more than a legal violation. Once we begin to see it in that way, morality becomes no more than legality and penance no more than formality. This, I think, is what has happened to a large part of our society and even of our own Catholic people, clergy included. It is certainly present in the silly notion that something is moral simply because it is legal. That is how abortion, which had been a serious crime, became overnight a constitutional right! This is how Hitler's "final solution" was justified. This attitude also reduces repentance to no more than a useless formalism demanding no real change in the depths of one's heart. The sacrament of Penance becomes a formality, an option that may give the illusion of comfort but involves no real necessity. It is a suicidal mockery of God's grace to think that we can sin, confess, and blithely sin again.

[16] Paul J. Achtemeier, *Romans* (Atlanta: John Knox Press, 1985), 99-100.

There is so much more that could be drawn from what Paul says in this letter, but space here is limited. Therefore, let me turn now to a few conclusions that we might draw about the pastoral strategy to cope with a culture of death.

Conclusions

First there is the particular responsibility belonging to bishops and priests. It is not only our words but our living examples that can have an enormous impact on our people. It is never sufficient for us to think that we have accomplished our goal when, in fact, all we may have done is win an argument or get a law modified. Those things are valuable, but they are hardly enough. Our mission is to speak to and transform hearts, not laws. Pope John Paul II calls upon teachers, catechists and theologians to reflect on and explain the reasons for the respect for human life. He calls upon all of us to preach the word in season and out of season. He says that his exhortation is directed especially to the bishops, whose task it is to ensure that this doctrine set forth in *Evangelium vitae* is faithfully handed on in its integrity (cf. *EV*, 82).

The question remains: Just how are we to teach it? How are we to ensure that it is handed on in its integrity? The real answer is found neither at an academic nor an administrative level. It is discovered deep within each one of us, and it emerges not as a verbal instruction, but as a living expression of the truth. If you are a priest, you should think of what you yourself have learned in your priesthood. You have seen the pain that people bear, and you have seen how that pain can deepen them in faith. You have seen people approach death, and in their dying you have experienced the power of God's grace. It is perhaps a paradox, but your experience of the death of others and your preparation for your own death can enable you to proclaim the reality of God's grace in the gift of life. If you wish to teach a "culture of life," then begin with what you yourself have already lived.

You can teach the truth of the creation of human life and the sacredness of human sexuality, not because of great psychological or theological theories on either, but far more because of the way in which you have chosen to live. Not only your words, but your actions as well can teach others of the seriousness and the wonder of the power to create life. Modern culture has turned sexuality into a pastime, a sales gimmick, a self-centered search for pleasure.

You can teach something different because of the way in which you choose to live. Celibacy is not a penance. It is a living sign of the sacredness of our power to transmit life. Trivialization of sexuality has led in the end to contempt of new life and the rejection of it as a burden and an interference with pleasure. Your respect for sexuality should be a sign of something totally different.

The real strategy resides in a way of life. We cannot live as though sin is not serious. It is deadly serious, and our lives must be signs of that both in our commitment to what is right and our acceptance of the need for repentance. We cannot act as though Christian life means keeping a set of rules and thereby attaining the reward of heaven. The fact is that the reward itself comes about only when we are truly and completely transformed into new life. We cannot teach all that Christ sends us to teach, and then live as though this world is what really matters.

When the rich young man[17] came to talk to Jesus, he wanted to know the secret of how to attain eternal life. He saw it as a matter of commandments and responses, but he seemed to know that there was still something missing. And then Jesus told him a truth that was absolutely simple, but to him seemed impossibly hard. He told him to hold on to nothing. Instead, just let go of everything, follow him and be one with God. In this his whole life would be transformed. He would be truly reborn, if only he would cease to think of himself and simply obey the will of the Father. Of him George MacDonald wrote:

> The Lord cared neither for isolated truth nor for orphaned deed. It was truth in the inward parts, it was the good heart, the mother of good deeds, He cherished....It was good men He cared about, not notions of good things, or even good actions, save as the outcome of life, save as the bodies in which the primary live actions of love and will in the soul took shape and came forth....
>
> Had he done as the Master told him, he would soon have come to understand. Obedience is the opener of eyes....The poor idea of living forever, all that commonplace minds grasp at for eternal life–(is) its mere concomitant shadow, in itself not worth thinking about. When a man is...one with God, what should he do but live forever?[18]

---

[17] Cf. Matt. 19:16-22.

[18] From *Unspoken Sermons: Second Series, The Way,* quoted from *George MacDonald: An Anthology,* by C. S. Lewis (London: G. Bles, 1946), 40 and 42.

This is the beginning of our strategy for overcoming the culture of death. It is to preach with courage the truth that we have received, but to express it most eloquently of all in the way in which we live.

CHAPTER 6

The Newest Reproductive Technologies: Applying Catholic Teaching[1]

PETER J. CATALDO, PH.D.

This analysis begins with a brief explanation of some of the newest reproductive technologies, then provides an overview of the dominant secular views of reproductive technologies, and concludes with an application of Catholic teaching to the technologies. Part of the application process will include the development of a criterion by which the teaching on the difference between assisting and replacing the conjugal act can be specifically applied. A metaphysical analysis using the concepts of principal causality, instrumental causality, and active condition is employed in order to define assistance and replacement. Once these terms are given ontological precision, a criterion can be formulated for judging specific procedures. A defense of Gamete Intrafallopian Transfer (GIFT) will also be given in light of the criterion. The theological and philosophical objections to GIFT are examined

[1] For their helpful comments on earlier versions, I would like to thank Albert S. Moraczewski, O.P., Germain Kopaczynski, OFMConv., Daniel O'Brien, and, especially for his assistance with the Latin quotations, Daniel Maher. However, responsibility for the content is mine alone.

and then evaluated from the point of view that they do not take into account the relation between principal and instrumental causality. The particular selection of procedures to be examined has been determined in part by the typical kinds of inquiries made to the Pope John Center consultation service.

Reproductive Technologies

It is estimated that 1 in 5 couples in the United States experiences infertility.[2] Infertility is usually regarded as the lack of conception after at least one year of unimpeded sexual intercourse. There can be many causes of infertility, ranging from low sperm count, to blocked fallopian tubes, to causes that are not demonstrable. What follows is a brief overview of nine types of technologies used to intervene against infertility.

In Vitro Fertilization (IVF)

In the world of reproductive technologies IVF cannot be characterized as "new." The first reported use of IVF was an experiment with rabbits in 1944.[3] In 1978 Louise Brown was the first baby born live from IVF. Even though IVF is not a new technology, I wish to include it in the overview because it will serve as a basic model for explaining other reproductive technologies. It is also important to begin with IVF because the Vatican's *Instruction on Respect for Human Life in its Origin and on the Dignity of Procreation (Donum vitae)*[4] uses IVF as the paradigm for morally unacceptable reproductive technologies and procedures. In the interests of simplicity for ethical evaluation, my use of the terms "technologies" and "procedures" will include both the actual process by which fertilization takes place in them and any other steps associated with that process, such as the collection of sperm. It should also be noted that the associated steps for any of the procedures can, in practice, include donor sperm, eggs, and surrogate mothers.

---

[2] *The Merck Manual of Diagnosis and Therapy*, Sixteenth Edition, ed. Robert Berkow, M.D. and Andrew J. Fletcher, M.B., B. Chir. (Rahway, N.J.: Merck Research Laboratories, 1992), 1768.

[3] Serena H. Chen, M.D. and Edward E. Wallach, M.D., "Five Decades of Progress in Management of the Infertile Couple," *Fertility and Sterility*, 62: 4 (1994), p. 670, note 53.

[4] Congregation for the Doctrine of the Faith, February 22, 1987: *Acta Apostolicae Sedis* 80 (1988), 70-102 (hereafter referred to by its Latin title, *Donum vitae*, and cited according to its outline divisions. The Vatican translation into English is available as *Respect for Human Life* (Boston: St. Paul Editions, n.d.); see also *Origins*, vol. 16, no. 40 (March 19, 1987), 697-711.

The IVF procedure usually begins with ovarian hyperstimulation in order to generate multiple mature eggs. The eggs are then "retrieved by direct needle puncture of the follicle, either transvaginally by ultrasound guidance or by laparoscopy."[5] Semen is usually collected by masturbation and then "washed," which is a process used to collect the most motile sperm. Sperm and eggs are then placed in a culture medium for fertilization. The resulting embryos are cultured for about 40 hours, at which time 3 to 4 embryos are transferred into the uterine cavity. A recent study of IVF, conducted in the United States and Canada by the Society for Assisted Reproductive Technology (SART), reported 24.1% pregnancies per retrieval of oocytes and 16.8% deliveries per retrieval.[6]

Gamete Intrafallopian Transfer (GIFT)

In this procedure eggs are produced and retrieved in the same manner as IVF. Sperm is collected, either by masturbation or through the use of a perforated Silastic sheath during sexual intercourse approximately two hours prior to the surgical phase, and then washed. The gametes are placed in a catheter separated by an air bubble (in a modified version) and transferred by laparoscopy into the distal fallopian tubes (point nearest the ovaries) for fertilization to take place at the natural site. The success rate for GIFT has been reported at 33.5% pregnancies per retrieval and 26.3% deliveries per retrieval.[7]

Low Tubal Ovum Transfer (LTOT)

This procedure, rather than transferring both male and female gametes, transfers only the woman's egg. The egg is collected by laparoscopy and replaced for fertilization in the lower portion of the fallopian tube close to the uterus. The couple engages in sexual intercourse before and after replacement of the egg. Two pregnancies resulting from LTOT have been reported.[8]

---

[5] *Merck Manual,* 1772.

[6] See "Assisted Reproductive Technology in the United States and Canada: 1992 Results Generated from the American Fertility Society/Society for Assisted Reproductive Technology Registry," *Fertility and Sterility,* 62:8 (1994), 1122.

[7] Ibid., 1124.

[8] See David S. McLaughlin, M.D., "A Scientific Introduction to Reproductive Technologies," in *Reproductive Technologies, Marriage and the Church,* ed. Donald G. McCarthy (Braintree, Mass.: Pope John Center, 1988), 63-64. LTOT is mentioned here primarily because it is usually compared to GIFT in the Catholic literature.

Pronuclear Stage Tubal Transfer (PROST) and Zygote Intrafallopian Transfer (ZIFT)

These procedures retrieve gametes and perform fertilization in the same manner as IVF. In PROST the pronuclear stage embryo is transferred into the fallopian tubes. This stage occurs 10-22 hours after sperm penetration of the ovum and marks the formation of two nuclei containing 23 chromosomes from the spermatazoon and 23 chromosomes from the oocyte. A 1987 study reported a rate of 26.9% pregnancies per transfer.[9] In the case of ZIFT, at 22-30 hours after initial penetration of the sperm the zygote is transferred into the fallopian tubes. The 1992 SART study shows 28.8% pregnancies per retrieval and 22.8% deliveries per retrieval using ZIFT.[10] PROST and ZIFT were developed originally to confirm and enhance the fertilization process in comparison to GIFT.[11]

Intrauterine Insemination (IUI)

This procedure directly transfers washed sperm into the uterine cavity. As described in a recent article in *Obstetrical and Gynecological Survey*, sperm is deposited "in the uterine cavity by means of a catheter that has been passed through the cervical canal. In this way, an increased number of sperm cells can be brought instantaneously to the proximity of the fertilization site, while the cervical barrier has been by-passed."[12] This procedure is performed intravaginally, intracervically, or pericervically. It has been shown that although IUI is the treatment of choice for some conditions, "the reported results remain controversial and there is still no consensus on its [IUI's] real efficacy and applications."[13]

Intracytoplasmic Sperm Injection (ICSI)

This is a microsurgical procedure in which sperm is collected, treated, and directly injected by means of a microinjection needle into eggs for fertilization in vitro. After fertilization occurs the zygotes are transferred into the uterus. ICSI has potential to resolve all forms of male infertility, but remains a new technique. A Belgian group has reported 16.1% pregnancies

[9] See Chen and Wallach, "Five Decades," p. 678, note 154.

[10] "Assisted Reproductive Technology," *Fertility and Sterility*, 62:8 (1994), 1124.

[11] Chen and Wallach, "Five Decades," 678.

[12] A.R. Martinez, et al., "Basic Questions on Intrauterine Insemination," *Obstetrical and Gynecological Survey*, 48:12 (1993), 818.

[13] Ibid., 811.

per cycle and 21.8% per replacement into the uterus.[14] Two other related procedures are Partial Zona Dissection (PZD) and Subzonal Sperm Insertion (SZI). In PZD a slit is made in the zona pellucida of the oocyte for fertilization then to take place in vitro. PZD has a high risk for polyspermy (fertilization of a single ovum by more than one spermatozoon) and detrimental effects for any developing zygote and embryo. In SZI several sperm are directly injected into the oocyte. This too has a high rate of polyspermy and poor pregnancy results as well, ranging from 2% to 11.9% per ovulation cycle.[15]

Natural Cycle Oocyte Retrieval Intravaginal Fertilization (NORIF)

In this procedure an egg is retrieved during a natural ovulation cycle without ovulatory hyperstimulation and is placed in a medium contained in a special vial along with washed sperm. The vial is sealed and placed in a sealed cryoflex envelope. The envelope and its contents are then placed in the vagina for a period of 48 hours to allow fertilization to take place. The vial is then removed and the embryo is extracted and transferred into the uterus. A pregnancy rate of 10% per cycle has been estimated.[16] Several advantages of NORIF over IVF have been cited in the opinion of its designers, including no multiple pregnancies, elimination of the pain and discomfort associated with ovarian hyperstimulation, minimum monitoring time for oocyte retrieval, and financial affordability to more couples.

Natural Procreative (NaPro) Technology

This method for infertility treatment was developed by Thomas Hilgers, M.D., Director of the Pope Paul VI Institute for the Study of Human Reproduction and of the institute's National Center for the Treatment of Reproductive Disorders. Dr. Hilgers defines NaPro Technology as "the use of one's medical, surgical and allied health energies in a way that is cooperative with the natural procreative systems."[17] The application of NaPro Technology to problems of infertility due to female factors is based on two premises: first, "infertility is only a symptom of underlying

[14] Mina Alikani, "Micromanipulation of Human Gametes for Assisted Fertilization," *Current Opinion in Obstetrics and Gynecology*, 5 (1993), 597.

[15] Ibid., 594-596.

[16] See M.L. Taymor et al., "Natural Oocyte Retrieval with Intravaginal Fertilization," *Obstetrics and Gynecology*, 80:5 (1992), 888-891.

[17] Thomas W. Hilgers, "Answers for Infertility," *Celebrate Life* (May-June 1995), 35.

organic and hormonal dysfunction or diseases;" second, success in the treatment of infertile couples can be found by treating the underlying disease process. Dr. Hilgers begins the evaluation of a patient by charting the woman's mucus symptoms using the Creighton Model of Natural Family Planning. He then performs "a thorough hormonal profile of the menstrual cycle, an ultrasound series to evaluate the anatomy of the ovary during the menstrual cycle, and a diagnostic laparoscopy."[18] Dr. Hilgers estimates a pregnancy rate of 50 to 75 percent following identification and treatment of the disease processes. Apparently, NaPro Technology does not treat infertility due to male factors.

Dominant Secular Views

Moral arguments for reproductive technologies take many forms, but two predominant justifications are made on the bases of personal autonomy and emotivism. A sampling of these views will provide a lay of the ethical landscape before considering the Catholic position. H. Tristram Engelhardt succinctly states the premise upon which the argument from personal autonomy is made:

> Next to one's own body, the sperm, ova, zygotes, and fetuses one produces are, in secular moral terms, primordially one's own. They are the extension of and fruit of one's own body. They are one's own to dispose of until they take possession of themselves as conscious entities, until one gives them a special standing in the community, until one transfers one's rights in them to another, or until they become persons. The sense of right here draws attention to the lack of others' authority to impose their will on such private choices.[19]

The primacy of individual autonomy is also evident in the ethical principles used by various commissions and committees on reproductive technologies. The Canadian Royal Commission on New Reproductive Technologies, for example, lists the principle of "Individual Autonomy" as the first principle in its "Ethical Framework and Guiding Principles." The commission's principles were used as the basis to justify IVF and IVF-related procedures. The commission stated the principle of autonomy in

[18] Ibid.
[19] H. Tristram Engelhardt, Jr., *The Foundations of Bioethics*, Second Edition (New York: Oxford Univ. Press, 1996), 256.

this way: "People should be free to choose how to lead their lives, particularly with respect to their bodies and fundamental commitments such as health, family, sexuality and work. This freedom must be limited if others are harmed, forced or coerced, or if social stability is undermined."[20] The 1995 Danish Council of Ethics, in its *Report on Assisted Reproduction,* noted that, of the five major ethical perspectives, the "autonomy-based perspective" is central to the Danish view of reproductive technologies:

> Based on the autonomy-based perspective, it would be counter to this tradition [of mutual tolerance], e.g. in relation to assisted reproduction, to issue bans based solely on narrow views that involve depriving people of the possibility of taking their own stance on whether or not the various forms of treatment are acceptable.[21]

The 1988 report by the United States Congress Office of Technology Assessment, *Infertility: Medical and Social Choices,* premised its "ethical considerations" on what it called "the right to reproduce."

> A fundamental aspect of much modern moral thinking is the significance of free and autonomous choices....When applied to an evaluation of techniques for preventing and treating infertility, the result is an emphasis on the moral significance of couples and individuals freely choosing to act in accordance with their own values....The right to reproduce is most often a liberty right in that it demands only that others do not interfere.[22]

The report of the American Fertility Society, *Ethical Considerations of the New Reproductive Technologies,* issued in 1986, was based upon three ethical principles held in tension: respect for autonomy, beneficence, and justice. Respect for autonomy was closely related in the report to the liberty rights of reproduction, including

[20] Royal Commission on New Reproductive Technologies, *Update* (Dec., 1993), 7.

[21] The Danish Council of Ethics, *Report on Assisted Reproduction,* trans. Tim Davies, B.A., M.A. (1995), 43. The five perspectives on reproductive technologies cited by the council are: the autonomy-based perspective; humanistic "Samaritan" perspective; individual-oriented conseqentialist perspective; community-oriented consequentialist perspective; and the Christian conservative perspective (see 41-42). The report explains that the humanistic "Samaritan" perspective is also central to the Danish view. This perspective will be mentioned below.

[22] United States Congress, Office of Technology Assessment, *Infertility: Medical and Social Choices,* OTA-BA-358 (Washington, D.C.: U.S. Government Printing Office, May, 1988), 205.

noncoital means of conception like IVF.[23] Another typical representation of the use of autonomy to justify reproductive technologies is reflected in this passage from an editorial in *The Economist*:

> If you want to bring busy-bodies out of the woodwork, sex works every time. There is something nasty in human nature that delights in regulating other people's sexual behaviour, whether procreative or purely pleasurable....In matters like this, not all beliefs can be argued away. Some people take it as an ethical truism that fiddling with the reproductive process is just plain wrong. If that is their belief they need not use the technique themselves, and they are free to argue with people who want to use it. But they should not be free to curtail the freedoms of others. To try and impose beliefs derived from faith on people who do not share them is odious.[24]

Notions of personal autonomy, such as the one advocated in the United States Supreme Court decision *Planned Parenthood of Southeastern Pennsylvania v. Casey*, are also used to justify virtually unlimited reproductive technology. The majority wrote: "At the heart of liberty is the right to define one's own concept of existence, of meaning, of the universe and of the mystery of human life."[25] On these grounds, the right to determine the meaning of one's existence ought to include the right to any form of reproductive technology, even if it entails selecting the sex and genetic characteristics of the offspring.[26] Finally, the statement of a Catholic Florida woman captures a view common to infertile couples. When interviewed about Catholic teaching in this area she said: "I am dead-set against the Catholic Church telling me what I can and cannot do regarding infertility...[e]specially when it's a chance to create life."[27]

The use of reproductive procedures is also defended in emotivistic terms. As with other issues in medical ethics, such as

---

[23] *Fertility and Sterility*, 46:3 (1986) (Supp. 1), 19S-20S; 4S. See the American Fertility Society's critique of *Donum vitae* in *Fertility and Sterility*, 49:2 (1988) (Supplement 1).

[24] "My Son, My Daughter," *The Economist* (January 30, 1993), 17.

[25] Reprinted in *Origins*, vol. 22, no. 8 (July 9, 1992), 117.

[26] This is the reasoning used by John Robertson in his "Procreative Liberty and the Control of Conception, Pregnancy and Childbirth," *Virginia Law Review*, 69 (1983), 450. See also his "Noncoital Reproduction and Procreative Liberty," in *The Ethics of Reproductive Technology*, ed. Kenneth D. Alpern, (New York: Oxford Univ. Press, 1992), 250.

[27] As reported by Jeffrey Good, "The Gift of Infertility?" *Jacksonville Times* (October 24, 1993), 5D.

physician-assisted suicide, there is a resurgence of emotivism. The contemporary philosopher, Alasdair MacIntyre, in his *After Virtue*, offers a clear and concise definition of the general theory of emotivism:

> Emotivism is the doctrine that all evaluative judgments and more specifically all moral judgments are *nothing but* expressions of preference, expressions of attitude or feeling, insofar as they are moral or evaluative in character....[M]oral judgments, being expressions of attitude or feeling, are neither true nor false; and agreement in moral judgment is not to be secured by any rational method, for there are none. It is to be secured, if at all, by producing certain non-rational effects on the emotions or attitudes of those who disagree with one. We use moral judgments not only to express our own feelings and attitudes, but also precisely to produce such effects in others.[28]

A major task of MacIntyre's book is to demonstrate his claim that "to a large degree people now think, talk and act *as if* emotivism were true, no matter what their avowed theoretical stand-point may be. Emotivism has become embodied in our culture."[29] To the extent that this is true of the culture in general, emotivism is accordingly gaining a stronghold in medical ethics, especially in the ethics of reproductive technologies. The celebrated *Warnock Report on Human Fertilisation and Embryology*, for example, gave primacy to moral feelings in comparison to rational argument.[30] In her introduction, Mary Warnock, for whom the *Report* was named and the Chair of the original committee, cites David Hume, the father of emotivism, as the authority in moral matters and approvingly quotes his famous line that morality is "more properly felt than judg'd of."[31] Moreover, the *Report* itself, and Warnock's introduction and conclusion, assert as universally true that

[28] Alasdair McIntyre, *After Virtue: A Study in Moral Theory* (Notre Dame: Univ. of Notre Dame Press, 1981), 11-12.

[29] Ibid., 21.

[30] See Mary Warnock, *A Question of Life: The Warnock Report on Human Fertilisation and Embryology* (New York: Basil Blackwell, 1985), 1-2.

[31] Ibid., viii. See David Hume, *A Treatise of Human Nature*, ed. L.A. Selby-Bigge, 2nd rev. ed. by P.H. Niddich (Oxford: Clarendon Press, 1978); especially: "Moral distinctions, therefore, are not the offspring of reason. Reason is wholly inactive, and can never be the source of so active a principle as conscience, or a sense of morals" (458); and "Morality, therefore, is more properly felt than judg'd of; tho' this feeling or sentiment is commonly so soft and gentle, that we are apt to confound it with an idea" (470).

questions of morality "are not susceptible of proof" and that "there is no such thing as a correct judgment."[32]

Consider also the many television news stories and programs on infertility and the newest reproductive technology, which feature the plight of particular infertile couples and their "miracle" babies. The format is predictable: the viewer meets an average, amiable couple and is told a story about their lives, marriage, and genuinely tragic circumstances that have left them childless. The viewer is then introduced to the technology of reproduction and the doctors who perform the procedures. The journey through the technological process is presented, culminating in the display of the mother or couple, the beautiful baby or babies, and their infectious joy.[33]

Narrative is also used effectively in the emotivistic approach. It is designed to evince the appropriate moral feelings and sentiments towards the infertile couple, and through those feelings, approval of the technology. One such storyteller and father typifies this emotivistic approach and its disdain for rational method and conceptual analysis in the issue. Writing about his daughter who was generated with IVF he says: "Dignity, zygotes, subversion, illicit, procreation. Words, words, words. The reality is Lily [his daughter], and she is holy beyond my comprehension and yours...how she came about doesn't make a whole lot of difference to me."[34] He too attempts to convince us of the moral rightness of his actions with his wife in and through their personal narrative, describing with tender prose how this daughter every day breaks his heart "into thousands of pieces."[35] What is morally decisive according to the emotivistic approach is the *desideratum*, i.e., the thing desired and its moral rectitude, precisely because it is desired. The end result creates such an irresistible emotivistic appeal that the moral rightness of the technological process by which the child is generated is asserted as obvious.

[32] Warnock, 2 and 96; see also Introduction, x. Apparently, the moral judgments in making these very statements are somehow exempt from their purview.

[33] See, for example, *NOVA*, "Test-Tube Babies: A Daughter for Judy." Original broadcast date: January 17, 1982.

[34] Brian Doyle, "The Church Shouldn't Prohibit Test-Tube Babies," *U.S. Catholic* (June 1992), 13.

[35] Ibid., 14.

Catholic Teaching on Reproductive Technologies

Catholic teaching denies neither personal autonomy nor the desire of couples to have children; rather, it anchors these goods in the creative love of God and in the objective structure of human nature. In *Evangelium vitae* John Paul II provides the foundation for the response to the attempted justification of reproductive technologies based upon absolute autonomy and emotivism. Referring to man's loss of the sense of God, the Holy Father states:

> He [man] no longer considers life as a splendid gift of God, something "sacred" entrusted to his responsibility and thus also to his loving care and "veneration". Life itself becomes a mere "thing", which man claims as his exclusive property, completely subject to his control and manipulation.
>
> Thus, in relation to life at birth or at death, man is no longer capable of posing the question of the truest meaning of his own existence nor can he assimilate with genuine freedom these crucial moments of his own history. He is concerned only with "doing," and using all kinds of technology, he busies himself with programming, controlling and dominating birth and death. Birth and death, instead of being primary experiences demanding to be "lived", become things to be merely "possessed" or "rejected".
>
> Moreover, once all reference to God has been removed, it is not surprising that the meaning of everything else becomes profoundly distorted. Nature itself, from being "*mater*" (mother), is now reduced to being "matter", and is subjected to every kind of manipulation.[36]

Contrary to the United States Supreme Court, man, absorbed as he is in today's culture with the question of "doing," is incapable of raising the prior question, posed by Pope John Paul II, of "the

---

[36] "*Sic tamquam eximium Dei donum non amplius iudicat vitam, rem quandam 'sacram' suae responsalitati ideoque amabili custodiae creditam suaeque 'venerationi'. Ipsa plane fit 'res', quam sibi veluti suum ipsius mancipium vindicat, gubernabile prorsus et tractabile.*

"*Proposita ideo ante oculos vita quae nascitur et quae moritur, non amplius valet homo interrogari de verissimo suae vitae sensu, accipiens videlicet vera cum libertate haec decretoria suae 'vitae' momenta. Eum solummodo 'faciundi' tenet cura, atque ad omnes artes se conferens, ortum obitumque supputare, temperare et gubernare sollicite contendit. Experientiae hae, quae primigeniae requirunt ut 'agantur', res fiunt potius quaedam, quas tantum 'possidere' aut 'respuere' intendit homo.*

"*Omissa ceterum omni necessitudinis ratione cum Deo, non cuiquam admiratio movebitur, quod omnium inde rerum significatio funditus detorta evadit ac natura ipsa, iam non amplius 'mater', potius ad quandam redacta est 'materiam' quibuslibet tractationibus obnoxiam*" (John Paul II, *Evangelium vitae* [March 25, 1995], section 22: *AAS* 87 [1995], 425). The English translation is available as *The Gospel of Life* (Vatican City: Libreria Editrice Vaticana, 1995).

truest meaning of his own existence." The pope's words show that the technological imperative—to possess technology is to use technology—is an imperative of doing. It ignores the imperative of man's existence and the exigencies it places on what is to be done with human life. But it is precisely the distinction between doing and man's existence that must be recognized and appreciated first before a proper evaluation of the question of reproductive technologies can be made. The rich relation between human existence and doing is what Catholic teaching on reproductive procedures preserves.

The many layers of Catholic teaching on reproductive technologies cannot be explored here. Instead the focus will be on the critical role of the conjugal act between spouses. Quoting from *Humanae vitae, Donum vitae* uses the following concept of the conjugal act, which will be assumed throughout this analysis: "'Indeed, by its intimate structure, the conjugal act, while most closely uniting husband and wife, makes them capable of the generation of new lives, according to laws inscribed in the very being of man and of woman.'"[37] This description of the conjugal act includes two components which will be assumed in my use of the term. One component is the physical act of coitus, the other is the causal power of the conjugal act to generate new human life. Both components are subsumed under the unitive and procreative meanings of the conjugal act. It is important to understand that the identification of the conjugal act in Catholic teaching is made by reference not only to coitus but also to the act's causal power.

At the core of Catholic teaching on reproductive technologies are two goods: (1) the conjugal love between spouses expressed in and through specific conjugal acts; and (2) the human dignity of the child, which requires that he or she be the fruit of the conjugal union between mother and father. *Donum vitae* makes very clear at the outset the anthropological premises underlying this teaching. The primacy of the conjugal act for evaluating reproductive technologies is rightly understood only in light of the composite unity of the human person, body and soul. As Archbishop Carlo Caffara has written, "Human sexuality is actually a constitutive part of the human person. In a certain real sense, sexuality is the human person, for in the final analysis, the

---

[37] *Donum vitae,* II, B, 4, a: "'*Etenim propter intimam suam rationem, coniugii actus, dum maritum et uxorem artissimo sociat vinculo, eos idoneos etiam facit ad novam vitam gignendam, secundum leges in ipsa viri et mulieris natura inscriptas'.*" Here *Donum vitae* is quoting Pope Paul VI, *Humanae vitae,* 12: *AAS,* 60 (1968), 488-489.

human person is not a being who *has* a body, but a being who *is* a body."[38] Thus the love between the spouses from which a child is generated, and in which God's creative act of love is shared, must be fully human, i.e., it must come about as a result of the procreative act unique to the physical-spiritual unity of the human person. "It is not enough," Caffara argues, "that this love between husband and wife simply sets in motion the process which can possibly lead to conception, as though the love-bond between them were some power *distinct from* and *outside* the procreative power God has given to us as embodied persons."[39] Reproductive technology cannot be morally evaluated according to a view of the marriage relationship that separates this relationship from the individual conjugal act of the spouses. The one act that is specific to, and conjointly fulfilled in, both the procreative and unitive goods of marriage is the conjugal act, as we see in *Gaudium et spes*:

> Marriage and married love are by nature ordered to the procreation and education of children. Indeed children are the supreme gift of marriage....
>
> Married couples should regard it as their proper mission to transmit human life and to educate their children; they should realize that they are thereby cooperating with the love of God the Creator and are, in a certain sense, its interpreters.[40]

The Council refers to "objective criteria" for "harmonizing married love with the responsible transmission of life" and states that these criteria are

> drawn from the nature of the human person and human action, criteria which respect the total meaning of mutual self-giving and human procreation in the context of true love; all this is possible only if the virtue of married chastity is seriously practiced.[41]

[38] Archbishop Carlo Caffarra, "The Moral Problem of Artificial Insemination," Edward J. Bayer, S.T.D., trans., *Linacre Quarterly*, 55:1 (1988), 39.

[39] Ibid.

[40] "*Matrimonium et amor coniugalis indole sua ad prolem procreandam et educandam ordinatur. Filii sane sunt praestantissimum matrimonii donum....*

"*In officio humanam vitam transmittendi atque educandi, quod tamquam propria eorum missio considerandum est, coniuges sciunt se cooperatores esse amoris Dei Creatoris eiusque veluti interpretes*" (Second Vatican Ecumenical Council, *Gaudium et spes*, December 7, 1965, section 50: *AAS* 58 [1966], 1070-1071). The English text is available in *Vatican Council II: The Conciliar and Post Conciliar Documents*, rev. ed., Austin Flannery, O.P., gen. ed. (Boston: St. Paul Editions, 1988).

[41] "[*C*]*omponendo amore coniugali cum responsabili vitae transmissione... obiectivis criteriis, ex personae eiusdemque actuum natura desumptis, determinari debet, quae integrum sensum mutuae*

Donum vitae restates the teaching of *Humanae vitae* and *Gaudium et spes*, viz., that the intrinsic ordering of the conjugal act toward procreation excludes the possibility of other sorts of acts having a proper relation to procreation. Using the *Code of Canon Law*, *Donum vitae* states:

> Thus, *fertilization is licitly sought when it is the result of a "conjugal act which is per se suitable for the generation of children to which marriage is ordered by its nature and by which the spouses become one flesh". But from the moral point of view procreation is deprived of its proper perfection when it is not desired as the fruit of the conjugal act, that is to say of the specific act of the spouses' union.*[42]

To say that the conjugal act has this *per se* relationship to procreation is at the same time to recognize that it is an exclusive relationship. If the procreative end (together with the unitive end) formally defines the nature of the conjugal act, then it cannot define some other act (such as IVF), which is different in kind, and in reference to which it could be said that a proper ordering exists between it and the procreative end.

This teaching can be further clarified by contrasting it with some typical distortions of the exclusive relationship between the conjugal act and procreation in Catholic teaching. These misrepresentations are one basis upon which justification is sought for those reproductive technologies found unacceptable in Catholic teaching. The teaching on the centrality of the conjugal act in relation to procreation cannot be legitimately interpreted as applying only to those cases of reproductive technology in which a conjugal act is performed, but not to those procedures that do not

---

donationis ac humanae procreationis in contextu veri amoris observant; quod fieri nequit nisi virtus castitatis coniugalis sincero animo colatur," ibid., 51.

[42] II, B, 4 a: "*Quare,* eo fecundatio licite appetitur, quae manat ex actu coniugali qui natura sua aptus sit 'ad prolis generationem, ad quem natura sua ordinatur matrimonium, et quo coniuges fiunt una caro'. Eadem vero procreatio tunc debita sua perfectione destituitur sub aspectu morali, cum animo non intenditur ut fructus coniugalis actus seu illius gestus qui est proprius unionis coniugum" (emphasis in original). The Latin and English texts of *Donum vitae* do not quote exactly the same portion of the *Code of Canon Law.* The Latin text of *Donum vitae* does not quote the phrase "*per se aptum*" from the *Code,* but substitutes the phrase "*natura sua aptus.*" However, the substitution makes no difference to the point that both phrases describe the ontologically essential ordering of the conjugal act to fertilization. Since there is no difference in meaning, and since the Vatican translation of "*natura sua aptus*" is "per se suitable," I will use the one phrase "*per se*" to characterize the ordering of the act to fertilization. See *Codex iuris canonici,* can. 1061, §1: "*Matrimonium inter baptizatos validum dicitur ratum tantum, si non est consummatum; ratum et consummatum, si coniuges inter se humano modo posuerunt coniugalem actum per se aptum ad prolis generationem, ad quem natura sua ordinatur matrimonium, et quo coniuges fiunt una caro.*" The English text of *Donum vitae* uses the translation of the *Code* prepared under the auspices of the Canon Law Society of America (Vatican City: Libreria Editrice Vaticana, 1983): "A valid marriage between

include the conjugal act. This interpretation implicitly denies the magisterial teaching that all procreation must, as a moral obligation, result from the conjugal act. As the examples above from *Gaudium et spes, Humanae vitae,* and *Donum vitae* show, it is not true that the moral norms regarding the procreation of new life are in force only if sexual intercourse is to be performed, and are therefore inapplicable for those cases in which life is generated outside of a conjugal act. Richard McCormick, S.J., suggests, for example, that the prohibition of procreation without the conjugal act is not clear in Church teaching and quotes William Daniel, S.J., who comments on section 12 of *Humanae vitae*: "All we learn from this passage...is that *if the conjugal act is performed* it should have these qualities: it should not be falsified in either of its essential 'significations.' This does not necessarily imply that if there is to be procreation it should be by means of a unitive act."[43]

McCormick also summarizes a similar interpretation of Catholic teaching made by G.B. Guzzetti, viz., that the inseparability of the unitive and procreative meanings is restricted to the conjugal act, and does not exist between the conjugal act and the generative process as such. "What one says about the conjugal act," McCormick writes, "does not necessarily apply when there is no question of the conjugal act."[44] However, in addition to being contrary to Catholic teaching, this position begs the question because it assumes that the inseparability between the unitive and the procreative meanings of the conjugal act is not a *per se* ordering of one aspect to the other—the very thing in question.

If it is assumed that the unitive and procreative meanings of the conjugal act are not intrinsically ordered toward each other, then any actual procreation need not be linked to the unitive aspect of the procreative tendency within the couple. However, since the two meanings are intrinsically ordered toward each other in the conjugal act, any actual procreation cannot be morally separated from that act. To see how the separation between the two meanings of the conjugal act is being assumed by the

baptized persons is called ratified only if it has not been consummated; it is called ratified and consummated if the parties have performed between themselves in a human manner the conjugal act which is per se suitable for the generation of children, to which marriage is ordered by its very nature and by which the spouses become one flesh."

[43] Richard A. McCormick, S.J., "Therapy or Tampering: The Ethics of Reproductive Technology and the Development of Doctrine," in *Bioethics,* 4th ed. by Thomas A. Shannon (Mahwah, N.J.: Paulist Press, 1993), 105. McCormick quotes from William Daniel, S.J., "In Vitro Fertilization: Two Problem Areas," *Australasian Catholic Record* 63 (1986), 31.

[44] Ibid. McCormick cites G.B. Guzzetti, *"Debolezza degli argomenti contro l'embryo-transfer,"* *Rivista di teologia morale* 17 (1985), pp. 72-73 note 19.

interpretation presented, consider Daniel's reference to the "unitive act" in the quotation above. The fact that it is mentioned as if it is something separate from the procreative meaning of the conjugal act assumes that there can be an act that stands alone as the "the unitive act." But if the unitive and the procreative meanings are inseparable, an independent "unitive act" is not possible. The unitive meaning of the conjugal act is not exclusively identified with marital coitus, as Daniel's position implies; rather, the conjugal act fulfills its unitive meaning only through its procreative meaning and its procreative meaning is fulfilled only through its unitive meaning. That is, the conjugal act is unitive only if the procreative ordination or tendency of that act is not deliberately thwarted or impeded, as part of the total, mutual gift of the spouses to each other. The act is procreative only if it is able to tend toward procreation according to the natural tendency within the couple and the nuptial meaning of the body, allowing the spouses to make a complete gift to each other as male and female in the fullness of their communion as persons.[45] Thus, the unitive meaning is not reducible to simple coitus and the procreative meaning is not reducible to reproduction.

Another common misrepresentation claims that the unitive and procreative meanings of the conjugal act may be broadly interpreted with respect to the total marriage relationship, allowing most any homologous reproductive technology on the basis that it would strengthen and maintain the marriage partnership. McCormick summarizes and suggests this interpretation stating that:

> [I]t might be sufficient if the *spheres* of the unitive and procreative are held together so that there is no procreation apart from marriage, and no full sexual intimacy apart from a context of responsibility for procreation....[Some] argue

[45] See Karol Wojtyla (John Paul II) on the intrinsic link between procreation and the conjugal act: "This is in fact the character of true conjugal love between two persons, a man and a woman, who have consciously taken the decision to participate in the whole natural order of existence, to further the existence of the species *Homo*" (*Love and Responsibility*, trans. H.T. Willets [New York: Farrar, Straus, Giroux, 1981], 53). For further sources on the theme of the nuptial meaning of the body and the language of the body see, for example: *Humanae vitae*, 9 and 13; *Familiaris consortio*, 19 and 32; *Donum vitae*, II, B, 4. See John Paul II's weekly general audiences related to the subject, especially the following: *Original Unity of Man and Woman: Catechesis on the Book of Genesis* (Boston: St. Paul Editions, 1981), 70-84, and *Reflections on Humanae Vitae: Conjugal Morality and Spirituality* (Boston: St. Paul Editions, 1984), 1-6; 29-34. For a good presentation of Pope John Paul II's theology of the body see Janet Smith, *Humanae Vitae: A Generation Later* (Washington, D.C.: Catholic Univ. of America Press, 1991), chapter 8.

that the unitive and procreative should be held together *within the relationship*; or, in more practical terms, just as contraceptive intercourse can be life giving (as nourishing the couple's life giving relationship), so in vitro fertilization can be unitive (as strengthening the relational good, the bond between the couple).[46]

In a similar vein Lisa Sowle Cahill argues that in Catholic teaching on marriage there is an emerging paradigm with two components. The first is that the partnership of the couple is primary in the nature of marriage. The other component is "that the biological structure of a sexual act is secondary to (not absent from) its moral meaning."[47] Cahill explains the effect of the paradigm with respect to reproductive technologies:

> Artificial assistance to conception within marriage, even when it circumvents sexual union, only makes sexual union secondary to the shared goal of parenthood and the partnership of the spouses....An each-and-every-act analysis of the 'inseparability' of sex, love, and procreation distorts the valid unity among them by tying that unity to specific sexual acts rather than to the marital relationship. The corporeal aspects of marriage and parenthood must be subsumed under the interpersonal meanings in order to have moral intelligibility.[48]

Cahill concludes that the primacy of the marriage relationship makes the biological manipulation of one or both of the spouses for the purpose of procreation morally acceptable.[49]

In fact, the relationship of the couple according to this view takes on the same sort of independence for which the central role of the conjugal act in Catholic teaching is criticized by Cahill and others. If the each-and-every-act analysis is wrong because no one aspect of marriage is independent from the others, then the same

[46] McCormick, "Therapy or Tampering," 107 and 117. See also Richard A. McCormick, *Health and Medicine in the Catholic Tradition* in *Health/Medicine and the Faith Traditions*, ed. Martin E. Marty and Kenneth L. Vaur (New York: Crossroad, 1984), 100-101. See *Fertility and Sterility*, 49:2 (1988) (Supplement 1), 1S; John W. Carlson, "*Donum Vitae* on Homologous Interventions: Is IVF-ET A Less Acceptable Gift than 'GIFT'?" *Journal of Medicine and Philosophy*, 14:5 (1988), 529.

[47] Lisa Sowle Cahill, "The Unity of Sex, Love and Procreation" in *Gift of Life: Catholic Scholars Respond to the Vatican Instruction*, ed. Edmund D. Pellegrino, John Collins Harvey, and John P. Langan (Washington, D.C.: Georgetown University Press, 1990), 141.

[48] Ibid., 142.

[49] Ibid., 143. See also Lisa Sowle Cahill, "Moral Traditions, Ethical Language, and Reproductive Technologies," *Journal of Medicine and Philosophy*, 14:5 (1988), 495-522.

criticism ought to apply to the broader interpretation, because on this view the partnership of the marriage, precisely as such, is described as though it has a real existence of its own. However, the marital relationship does not have a real existence abstracted from the individual acts that instantiate it. This does not mean that the marital relationship is reducible or equivalent to its instantiating, individual acts. Rather, it means that the relationship of the spouses cannot be an entity separate from the concrete actions of the spouses. The marital relationship comes into being and has an identifiable presence in and through the individual acts of the spouses. If the marital relationship has no real being as an abstracted entity, but only in and through individual acts, then it follows that the relationship can be more fully realized in some of those acts than it can in others. The one act, among all the possible acts, in and through which the essence of the relationship is realized, is the conjugal act.[50] Cahill's position does not merely claim the primacy of the marital relationship over the sexual act, but also that the relationship itself is essentially identified by its unitive dimension. However, there are two inseparable goods constituting the essence of marriage: the unitive and procreative goods. The conjugal act is the one act by which that essence is realized.[51]

Assisting vs. Replacing the Conjugal Act: The Metaphysics of Defining and Applying the Terms

Donum vitae shows that the decisive question for evaluating the moral acceptability or unacceptability of reproductive procedures, is whether fertilization is obtained by a conjugal act or not. Adopting the teaching of Pius XII, *Donum vitae* makes a critical distinction for deciding this question. It is the distinction

---

[50] See Bruno Schüller, S.J., "Paraenesis and Moral Argument in *Donum Vitae*," in *Gift of Life*, 87-88, who makes a mistake similar to McCormick and Cahill by not recognizing the ontological difference between the reduction of spousal love to the individual conjugal act and the fulfillment of spousal love in the conjugal act.

[51] Cahill states that a couple's "partnership expressed sexually is a relationship continuing over time, composed of many acts along a continuum" ("Moral Traditions," 515). But "composed" here is not understood as an instantiation of the relationship. Rather, Cahill means that acts are redefined as relationships, for example: "Homologous methods permit a couple to retain the constitutive physical relationship of marriage, i.e., sexual intercourse, the constitutive physical relationship of parenthood, i.e., genetic reproduction, and the physical relationship which unites spousehood and parenthood, i.e., a mutual genetic contribution to offspring" (516). In each case an act (voluntary or involuntary) is regarded as a relationship.

between a procedure that "'seeks to assist the conjugal act either in order to facilitate its performance or in order to enable it to achieve its objective once it has been normally performed'" and a procedure that *substitutes for or replaces* the act.[52]

It is important to interpret the meaning of substitution or replacement in this context as referring not simply to (1) the elimination of the physical act of marital coitus, but also to (2) the usurpation of the proper causality of the conjugal act beyond coitus, even though the act may have been performed and the semen collected in a morally acceptable way. Since assistance to the conjugal act includes assistance to the generative process as the natural objective beyond the physical act of coitus, the meaning of substitution or replacement must also refer to that same process beyond coitus. I will presume both meanings of substitution and replacement throughout my analysis. Procedures that *assist* the conjugal act preserve the essential link between the conjugal act and procreation as the beginning and end points of a process. Those that *replace* the conjugal act sever the link.

Based on this distinction there are some procedures that would, in principle, be morally acceptable (*Donum vitae*, II, B, 6). But how do we know which procedures assist and which replace? Without some clear criterion, the line between assisting and replacing in many cases can be obscure. The moral evaluation of IVF and IVF-based procedures might be straightforward, but what about a procedure like GIFT or others yet to be developed? The question whether they assist or replace the conjugal act needs to be answered. The *Ethical and Religious Directives for Catholic Health Care Services*, which echoes *Donum vitae*, does not answer the question. According to the *Directives*, genuine assistance does not separate the unitive and procreative ends of the conjugal act, but the text does not state by what criterion this is to be determined in particular procedures. Directive 38 reads: "When the marital act of sexual intercourse is not able to attain its procreative purpose,

---

[52] *Donum vitae*, II, B, 7: " 'actum coniugalem adiuvare studet, sive ut facilius expleatur, sive ut idem, iam rite expletus, finem suum assequi possit.'" Here *Donum vitae* is quoting Pius XII's *Discourse to those taking part in the 4th International Congress of Catholic Doctors*, September 29, 1949: *AAS* 41 (1949), 560. See also his *Discourse to those taking part in the Second Naples World Congress on Fertility and Human Sterility*, May 19, 1956: *AAS* 48 (1956), 471-473 and *Donum vitae*, II, B, 6: "-Conscientia moralis, igitur, 'non neccessario damnat usum quorumdam mediorum artificialium eo unice spectantium, ut actus naturalis facilius perficiatur, utque idem actus rite expletus finem suum consequi possit'. Quare, si medium technicum faciliorem reddit actum coniugalum aut eum adiuvat ad fines suos naturales assequendos, licite adhiberi potest. Si, ex contrario, est substitutivum actus conjugalis, lege morali prohibetur." The internal quotation in this passage is also from Pius XII's September 29 *Discourse*.

assistance that does not separate the unitive and procreative ends of the act, and does not substitute for the marital act itself, may be used to help married couples conceive."[53] In like manner, the *Catechism of the Catholic Church* declares morally unacceptable techniques that "disassociate the sexual act from the procreative act."[54] These and similar texts in *Donum vitae* represent a further description of the distinction between assistance and replacement, but the conceptual mechanism or criterion by which the distinction can be applied to procedures is not addressed. I would like to propose a criterion that I believe is faithful to the teaching.

In order to present a criterion for conceptual precision distinguishing between replacing and assisting an act, it will be essential to employ the concept of causality from metaphysics.[55] Many critics of Catholic teaching would likely eschew any use of a metaphysical concept of causality with respect to reproductive technologies because they recognize only a scientific notion of causality. Nevertheless, the fact that a child simply is and has being, as distinct from the fact of its being a zygote, an embryo, or a fetus, cannot be denied. This prior metaphysical fact is integral to the ethical evaluation of the issue. A metaphysical analysis must be consistent with the scientific facts of infertility treatment, and is needed to provide an ontological ordering of those facts so that the ethical analysis can be performed.[56]

There are many varied causes of the new life generated by any given reproductive procedure. The task of making a criterion is not simply one of finding a method that first identifies the material and biological causes of fertilization in various procedures, and then determines on that basis whether the procedure assists or replaces the conjugal act. The conjugal act is a cause of the very being of the child. This act not only brings

---

[53] National Conference of Catholic Bishops, *Ethical and Religious Directives for Catholic Health Care Services*, approved November 1994, published March 1995.

[54] *Catechism of the Catholic Church*, English translation (Mahwah, N.J.: Paulist Press, 1994), no. 2377. The two acts mentioned respectively refer to coitus and fertilization.

[55] Aristotelian-Thomistic metaphysics will be employed since it corresponds well to Catholic teaching. Cf. Cynthia B. Cohen, "Give Me Children or I Shall Die!: New Reproductive Technologies and Harm to Children," *Hastings Center Report*, 26:2 (1996), 19-27 for a recent metaphysical analysis of reproductive technologies. Cohen examines the question of the interests of children not yet existing. However, the analysis is internally inconsistent in several respects. See also Ronald Dworkin, *Life's Dominion: An Argument about Abortion, Euthanasia, and Individual Freedom* (New York: Random House, 1994), 77-78.

[56] For a good summary of the various interpretations of the relation of Thomistic metaphysics to modern science, see Benedict Ashley, O.P., *Theologies of the Body: Humanist and Christian* (Braintree, Mass.: Pope John Center, 1995, reprint), 226-232.

about the meeting of male and female gametes, but much more the being of a new life in his or her totality, both actual and potential. Thus, a criterion that determines whether the conjugal act is assisted or replaced needs to recognize that the kind of causality the act exercises is not only physical causality as studied by biological science. Metaphysics provides an approach to the question of the conjugal act's causality specifically from the point of view of that which influences the child's act of existing. Since reproductive technologies affect the coming to be of the child, a metaphysical starting-point is appropriate and important.[57]

The general concepts of "principal cause (or agent)," "instrumental cause," and "active condition" are particularly suited to designing a criterion for applying the Church's distinction between assistance and replacement. A brief explanation of the concepts is needed before formalizing a criterion. A principal cause can be defined as "one that is *per se* responsible for whatever effect it produces," and which acts by its own power.[58] The principal agent, St. Thomas Aquinas explains, "works of itself. And therefore the power of the principal agent exists in nature completely and perfectly: whereas the instrumental power has a being that passes from one thing into another, and is incomplete...."[59] A principal cause is known as a *per se* cause since it acts of itself and causes what the effect is as such and substantially.[60] Thus, the principal cause is necessarily (*per se*) ordered to its effect and the effect has an essential likeness to the cause: "The principal cause works by the power of its form, to which form the effect is likened."[61] Aquinas' typical example of a principal cause is the builder of a house. The builder is the principal cause since as a builder the person has a *per se* relationship to the house. The house is likened to the art in the

[57] See John Paul II, *Love and Responsibility*, 52: "[I]f the sexual urge has an existential character, if it is bound up with the very existence of the human person—that first and most basic good—then it must be subject to the principles which are binding in respect of the person."

[58] Robert J. Kreyche, *First Philosophy* (New York: Henry Holt, 1959), 238.

[59] "[*P*]er se operatur. Et ideo virtus principalis agentis habet permanens et completum esse in natura: virtus autem instrumentalis habet esse transiens ex uno in aliud, et incompletum" (Thomas Aquinas, *Summa Theologiae*, III, 62, 4, corp.). Hereafter this will be cited as *ST*. Latin text is the Leonine critical edition, 1 vol. (Alba, Italy: *Editiones Paulinae*, n.d.). The English translation herein is *Summa Theologica*, rev. ed., trans. Fathers of the English Dominican Province (New York: Benziger Brothers; reprint, Westminster, Md.: Christian Classics, 1981).

[60] See *ST*, III, 56, 1, *ad* 2; Thomas Aquinas, *De Malo*, 4, 3, *corp*.; 1, 3, *ad* 2; 1, 3, *ad* 3.

[61] "*Principalis quidem operatur per virtutem suae formae, cui assimilatur effectus*" (*ST*, III, 62, 1, *corp*.).

builder's mind. Other qualities of the builder, on the other hand, are accidental causes of the house, such as the fact that the builder might be a musician or a grammarian.[62] The conjugal act is described in terms of *per se* causality in *Donum vitae* where it states that the conjugal act is "'per se suitable for the generation of children to which marriage is ordered by its nature and by which the spouses become one flesh.'"[63] The conjugal act of the spouses is aptly suited as a principal cause since both spouses act together as principal agents in an action ordered to the effect of the existence of a new human life which, as such, is an effect that has an essential likeness to the human nature of the parents.[64] Thus, the spouses, in and through their conjugal act, are the conjoined principal causes of the child. This is what is meant by the description of the conjugal act as the principal cause of fertilization.

There is an important distinction between a principal cause or agent and an instrumental cause:

> An instrument has a twofold action; one is instrumental, in respect of which it works not by its own power but by the power of the principal agent: the other is its proper action, which belongs to it in respect of its proper form: thus it belongs to an axe to cut asunder by reason of its sharpness, but to make a couch, in so far as it is the instrument of an art. But it does not accomplish the instrumental action save by exercising its proper action: for it is by cutting that it makes a couch.[65]

Two aspects of the instrumental cause must be noted. First, an instrumental cause or instrument possesses a form or nature of its own, according to which it is intelligible. Secondly, it is in and through the instrument's nature that it is used precisely as an

---

[62] See Thomas Aquinas, *Commentary on Aristotle's Physics,* trans. R. J. Blackwell, R. J. Spath, and W. E. Thirlkel (New Haven: Yale Univ. Press, 1963), #214.

[63] *Donum vitae,* II, B, 4; see footnote 42, p. 13 above. The other definition of the conjugal act (as capacitating husband and wife for the generation of new lives mentioned earlier (footnote 37, p. 11 above) expresses the same meaning as "per se suitable." Because he does not recognize the ontological dimension of the conjugal act, Schüller ("Paraenesis," 92) erroneously reduces the meaning of "capacitates" to biological capacity.

[64] The principal causality of the spouse's act is, of course, relative to God's causal power as First Cause.

[65] "[*I*]*nstrumentum habet duas actiones: unam instrumentalem, secundum quam operatur non in virtute propria, sed in virtute principalis agentis; aliam autem habet actionem propriam, quae competit sibi secundum propriam formam; sicut securi competit scindere ratione suae acuitatis, facere autem lectum inquantum est instrumentum artis. Non autem perficit actionem instrumentalem nisi exercendo actionem propriam; scindendo enim facit lectum*" (*ST,* III, 62, 1, *ad* 2). See also *ST,* I, 45, 5, *corp., Supp.,* 70, 3, *corp.,* and Thomas Aquinas, *De Veritate,* Vol. 3, 27, 4, *corp.*

instrument. Thus, the effect is not produced in virtue of the instrument but by means of the instrument and in virtue of the power of the principal cause. The being of the instrumental cause insofar as it is a cause is incomplete because its causality is transient, conveying the causal power of one thing to another, whereas the being of the principal cause is complete since it causes of itself.[66] An instrumental cause by definition, then, is something other than, and extrinsic to, the principal cause or agent, which uses the instrument to bring about an effect.

A further distinction must be made between (A) producing an effect through instrumental causality in the sense of a one-to-one relation, such as the pen being used by the one writing, and (B) producing an effect by the instrumental use or application of something that acts with its own principal causality, e.g. the transfusion of blood to produce health.[67] Aquinas' view of the sexual organs as instruments of the soul in *Summa Contra Gentiles*, III, 126, 2 is itself an example of the instrumental application of a natural cause. In this case the soul acts as the principal agent which makes an instrumental application of the sexual organs to effect a "carnal union."[68]

The concepts of assistance and replacement in *Donum vitae* can be interpreted according to the language of principal and instrumental causality. One requirement for something being assistance to the conjugal act is that the act remain the principal cause of fertilization. If the procedure itself or any part of it usurps the conjugal act's causal power, or the conjugal act is used only to obtain sperm, then the conjugal act has been replaced in its proper function as the principal cause. Reproductive procedures that provide genuine assistance are those that constitute the instrumental causes to the principal cause, the conjugal act. The instrumentality of these procedures is a combination of the two types of instrumental causes. The natural, principal causality of the

---

[66] See *ST*, III, 62, 4, *corp.*

[67] See George P. Klubertanz, S.J., *Introduction to the Philosophy of Being*, 2nd ed. (New York: Appleton-Century-Crofts, 1963), 152.

[68] "*Adhuc. Cum membra corporis sint quaedam animae instrumenta, cuiuslibet membri finis est usus eius: sicut et cuiuslibet alterius instrumenti*" (*Summa Contra Gentiles*, III, 126). Hereafter this work will be cited as *SCG*. Latin text is the Leonine Manual Edition (Rome: Desclée & Co., 1934). English text: "Again, since bodily organs are the instruments of the soul, the end of each organ is its use, as is the case with any other instrument" (trans. Vernon J. Bourke [Notre Dame: Univ. of Notre Dame Press, 1956], vol. 3:2, p. 155). Schüller (93) equivocates between Aquinas' term "instruments" and the term "techniques," which is found in *Donum vitae*, in an attempt to use *SCG*, III, 126 as a justification of illicit procedures.

conjugal act is used and applied for its own fulfillment (B above) by means of other various instrumental causes (A above).

The concept of an "active condition" is also useful for making a criterion to identify the lines of causality in the moral evaluation of reproductive procedures. George Klubertanz, S.J., defines an active condition as that "which removes a hindrance that prevents another agent from acting."[69] In a similar vein, Robert Kreyche describes the role of an active condition as making "it possible for a cause to exercise its activity. In general we may define a condition as a circumstance or set of circumstances that makes it possible for something to operate as a cause."[70] Turning on a light switch is an example of an active condition. This act closes a circuit, enabling a light bulb to produce light. This concept of an active condition describes another aspect of the causal relations in the notion of assisting, facilitating, and enabling the conjugal act found in the Church's teaching. Procedures that assist the conjugal act can also be said to supply the active condition(s) for the act to function as the principal cause of fertilization. Any criterion that applies the teaching to procedures would need to distinguish those that provide active conditions from those that do not. In other words, there is a difference between procedures that provide active conditions, which remove a hindrance specific to the natural causality of the conjugal act, and procedures that remove a hindrance only accidentally, as a result of creating a whole new line of causality for fertilization.

The reproductive technologies analyzed here affect the objective of the conjugal act. For this reason it is critical to note that the criterion proposed below for morally evaluating procedures centers on the way in which fertilization itself takes place in the procedures. The act of fertilization is pivotal in *Donum vitae* for determining whether a procedure has replaced the conjugal act. With respect to assistance for what is called the "natural purpose," "proper end," or "natural objectives" of the conjugal act,[71] *Donum vitae* focuses on those specific causes and conditions that bring about the act of fertilization itself. Accordingly, the criterion has been formulated on that basis. This is also why *Donum vitae* explicitly emphasizes the fact that in IVF fertilization occurs outside the body.[72] Referring to IVF, *Donum vitae* states,

---

[69] Klubertanz, *Philosophy of Being*, 162.

[70] Kreyche, *First Philosophy*, 236.

[71] See *Donum vitae*, II, B, 6.

[72] For an analysis of the extracorporeal dimension of artificial procreation, see Elio

"Fertilization achieved outside the bodies of the couple remains by this very fact deprived of the meanings and the values which are expressed in the language of the body and in the union of human persons."[73]

> Homologous IVF and ET [embryo transfer] is brought about outside the bodies of the couple through actions of third parties whose competence and technical activity, determine the success of the procedure. Such fertilization entrusts the life and identity of the embryo into the power of doctors and biologists and establishes the domination of technology over the origin and destiny of the human person. Such a relationship of domination is in itself contrary to the dignity and equality that must be common to parents and children.
> Conception *in vitro* is the result of the technical action that presides over fertilization.[74]

If and when fertilization is successful in IVF, it is so precisely because of active conditions that are outside and independent of the body. Thus, in the language of *Donum vitae*, fertilization has been determined by technical action. Given the pivotal role of fertilization in *Donum vitae* for making ethical evaluation, any criterion for distinguishing between procedures that assist and procedures that replace must draw the line at the *immediate* causal factors within the procedures—both causes and active conditions—that bring about fertilization itself. Whether these factors are due to the procedure or not is the question. By contrast, if the line were not drawn at fertilization, then the distinction between assistance and replacement would collapse. By not beginning a moral evaluation with the factors of fertilization itself, any third party action (as will be shown below) interposing itself at any point between the conjugal act and fertilization could arguably be considered as replacing the causal action of the conjugal act.

Sgreccia, "Moral Theology and Artificial Procreation in Light of Donum Vitae," trans. Cristia Demagistris, in *Gift of Life*, 115-135.

[73] *Donum vitae*, II, B, 4, b: "*Fecundatio quae extra corpus coniugum obtineatur, ob id ipsum tum significationibus tum valoribus caret, quae corporum lingua atque coniunctione personarum humanarum exprimuntur.*"

[74] *Donum vitae*, II, B, 5: "*Methodus FIVET homologa ad actum deducitur extra coniugum corpus, opera aliorum, a quorum scientia atque technica arte prosper exitus interventus dependet; eadem vitam identitatemque embryonum humanorum in potestatem redegit medicorum atque biologorum, sicque rei technicae dominatum quemdam in personae humanae originem et sortem instaurat. Huiusmodi dominatus suapte natura contradicit dignitati et aequalitati, quae parentibus et filiis communes esse debent.*"

"*Conceptio in vitro est effectus actionis technicae, per quem evenit fecundatio.*" See also Pontifical Council for Pastoral Assistance to Health Care Workers, *Charter for Health Care Workers*, 1995, section 24.

Extrapolating from *Donum vitae* and considering the causal concepts examined above, the following definitions for replacement and assistance may be given: *A procedure replaces the conjugal act if either coitus is not performed, or the conjugal act is not the principal* (per se) *cause of fertilization itself. A procedure assists the conjugal act if it supplies the instrumental causes and active condition(s) for the conjugal act to function as the principal (*per se*) cause of fertilization itself.* A criterion for morally evaluating specific procedures consistent with the definitions would be: *A procedure replaces the conjugal act if it determines, of itself, and immediately, the success of fertilization. A procedure assists the conjugal act if it does not determine, of itself, and immediately, the success of fertilization, but rather allows fertilization to take place under immediate causal factors that are natural.* This criterion covers both types of assistance in the teaching, viz., assistance to the performance of the conjugal act itself and to the attainment of its objective.

Assisting vs. Replacing the Conjugal Act: Application to Specific Procedures

No conjugal act obtains in either of the following cases: single persons using reproductive technologies; or the collection of the husband's sperm by masturbation for various procedures. Any such cases are *ipso facto* morally unacceptable. These cases replace the conjugal act in the first sense defined above, viz., they eliminate the physical act of marital coitus. Applying the criterion in cases where the sperm would be collected morally (explained below) but used in in vitro fertilization (IVF), pronuclear stage tubal transfer (PROST), zygote intrafallopian transfer (ZIFT), and intracytoplasmic sperm injection (ICSI) results in the conclusion that the conjugal act is replaced by them in the second sense defined above, viz., they usurp the proper causality of the conjugal act beyond coitus, even though the act may have been performed and the semen collected in a morally acceptable way. The technical activity of the doctors and the active conditions of the procedures would reduce the conjugal act to something other than the principal cause of fertilization since the immediate causal factors of fertilization in these procedures represent an irreversible discontinuance of the causal chain of events that begin with the conjugal act. For example, in IVF the gametes meet only because they are in a culture medium contained in a petri dish; in ICSI fertilization occurs within a culture medium and as the result of the microinjection of a spermatazoon.

Moreover, extra embryos are routinely frozen for these procedures, discarded, or are used in experimentation. These practices constitute the moral equivalent of abortion.[75] In these technologies the zygote and embryo are also externalized, placing their lives at additional risk. Natural cycle oocyte retrieval intravaginal fertilization (NORIF) replaces the conjugal act even though in a certain sense it could be said that fertilization takes place within the body, even if the sperm was collected morally. Fertilization itself is caused by the technical action of both the doctors and the active conditions within the procedure.

As with any of the procedures mentioned, intrauterine insemination (IUI) performed with masturbation replaces the conjugal act in the first sense. However, if the sperm is collected with a perforated Silastic sheath in a conjugal act, fertilization need not be determined by the technical actions of the procedure. The washing of sperm and placement of it in the uterine cavity by means of a catheter do not in and of themselves cause fertilization. They are active conditions by which the original conjugal act is enabled to exercise its causal power for fertilization, as it would were the physiological obstacle not present. Moreover, *Donum vitae* does not absolutely reject homologous artificial insemination (HAI), which could also be called homologous IUI. First, *Donum vitae* defines HAI as "the technique used to obtain a human conception through the transfer into the genital tracts of a married woman of the sperm previously collected from her husband."[76] The document then describes the condition under which HAI would be acceptable: "*Homologous artificial insemination within marriage cannot be admitted except for those cases in which the technical means is not a substitute for the conjugal act but serves to facilitate and help so that the act attains its natural purpose.*"[77] Applying the criterion to IUI shows that this procedure used with a conjugal act fulfills the condition under which homologous artificial insemination is morally acceptable in *Donum vitae*. As indicated above, the conjugal act would remain the principal cause of fertilization with the technical actions of the procedure functioning as active

---

[75] See *Donum vitae*, II, Introduction.

[76] Ibid., *5 note: "Seminatio artificialis homologa: *ars technica eo respiciens, ut humanus conceptus habeatur deponendo in viis genitalibus coniugatae mulieris semen mariti, antea collectum.*"

[77] Ibid., II, B, 6: "Seminatio artificialis homologa intra ambitum matrimonii admitti nequit, excepto casu in quo apparatus technicus non sit substitutivus actus coniugalis, sed se praebeat ut adiumentum ad naturalem eius finem facilius assequendum."

conditions and instrumental causes of the conjugal act's *per se* causality. An application of the criterion to NaPro Technology and low tubal ovum transfer (LTOT) shows that they are in accordance with Catholic teaching. The conjugal act remains the principal cause of fertilization itself in both cases. NaProTechnology does not even address fertilization itself, and LTOT only provides an active condition that removes a hindrance to the positioning of the egg prior to the conjugal act.

Gamete intrafallopian transfer (GIFT) performed with masturbation would replace the conjugal act in the first sense. Absent a specific magisterial teaching at the time of this writing, I believe that GIFT with a conjugal act assists that act because it remains the principal (*per se*) cause of fertilization itself. The procedure provides the active conditions and instrumentality by which the conjugal act is able to exercise its causality. The preparation of the sperm and the replacement of the male and female gametes by catheter into the distal portion of the fallopian tube are active conditions, whereby hindrances to fertilization are removed, consistent with the natural causality of the conjugal act. The whole fertilization process naturally occurs within the fallopian tube beginning with the successful fusion of a spermatozoon and ovum. GIFT provides the by-pass or removal of the hindrances and obstacles within their actual environment so that the causal process may proceed within that same environment. Unlike IVF and the other procedures that replace the conjugal act, in GIFT fertilization itself takes place within the immediate, natural conditions that are essentially the same as those in which a reproductive pathology is not present.[78] None of the steps in the procedure actually cause fertilization itself. IVF-based procedures, on the other hand, remove hindrances by irreversibly discontinuing the natural causal process and producing a new line of causality. These procedures do not introduce genuine active conditions but rather reduce the natural causality of the conjugal act to that of supplying the gametes for fertilization, which takes place completely separate from the natural causal action of the conjugal act.

Moreover, the use of a perforated Silastic sheath by the husband to collect semen for the procedure does not prevent a

---

[78] See Donald G. McCarthy, "Gift? Yes," *Ethics & Medics*, vol. 18, no. 9 (1993), 3-4; "Response" and "Pastoral Concerns," in *Reproductive Technologies, Marriage and the Church*, ed. Donald G. McCarthy (Braintree, Mass.: Pope John Center, 1988) 140-145 and 174-182. See also James J. Mulligan, *Choose Life* (Pope John Center, 1991), 226-240.

conjugal act. The conjugal act is complete because semen is deposited by the husband and the spouses make the essential self-gift to each other.[79] The natural activity of the collected semen is assisted by the active conditions of the procedure. Rather than incapacitating the conjugal act, the use of a perforated Silastic sheath is an active condition by which the causality of the act is continued. The use of a perforated sheath in GIFT does not suppress the act's unitive and procreative capacity, but enables the continuation of the conjugal act's causality. Nor is there a moral need to perform a sheath-free conjugal act either before or after the one performed with a perforated sheath, as if the sperm collected in the sheath is somehow not part of a complete conjugal act. Since the GIFT procedure assists in the manner described above, there is one conjugal act and the collected sperm is a part of one and the same act.[80]

Objections to GIFT: A Response

There seem to be two related sorts of criticisms against GIFT. One criticism is of the ontological sort. GIFT has been criticized from this perspective on the grounds that many of the technical actions in the procedure, especially the placement of the gametes by means of a catheter, have their own intelligibility and unity independent of the marital act.[81] They are such that they have no intrinsic relation to the marital act, and can function and be understood separate from the conjugal act. The very being of the actions in GIFT is thought not to depend upon the marital act but rather to be constituted separate from the marital act. The fact that the procedure could be conducted successfully by using sperm not obtained from the conjugal act, including sperm not from the husband, is thought to show that the marital act is not essential to

---

[79] See Gerald Kelly, S.J., *Medico-Moral Problems* (St. Louis: Catholic Hospital Association of the United States and Canada, 1958), 242: "The determining factor of true coitus is ejaculation into the vagina."

[80] See Orville N. Griese, *Catholic Identity in Health Care: Principles and Practice* (Braintree, Mass.: Pope John Center, 1987), 44-49. See Carlson, "*Donum Vitae* on Homologous Interventions," 532-533 for a criticism of the need to construct a "moral union" between the replacement of the spouse's gametes and a conjugal act *via* the performance of a sheath-free marital act either prior or subsequent to the procedure.

[81] See John Haas, "Pastoral Concerns: Procreation and the Marital Act," in *Reproductive Technologies, Marriage and the Church*, ed. Donald G. McCarthy (Braintree, Mass.: Pope John Center, 1988), 166-167, 178-179; "Gift? No!," *Ethics & Medics*, vol. 18, no. 9 (September, 1993), 2-3; William E. May, "Catholic Teaching on the Laboratory Generation of Human Life," in *The Gift of Life*, ed. Marilyn Wallace, R.S.M., Ph.D. and Thomas Hilgers, M.D. (Omaha, Neb.: Pope Paul VI Institute Press, 1990), 88; Donald DeMarco, *Biotechnology and the Assault on Parenthood* (San Francisco: Ignatius Press, 1991), 225-238.

achieving fertilization in GIFT. Likewise, the technical actions in GIFT create the possibility that the husband's and wife's gametes could be donated to other couples or never used at all. These sorts of possibilities are advanced as confirmation of the essential independence of GIFT from the conjugal act.

The other type of criticism of GIFT could be called the cumulative threshold objection. The point of this objection is that the technical actions involved in the procedure reach a number that irreparably disrupts the conjugal act in its several integral dimensions–physical, psychological, and spiritual.[82] The number of discrete steps in the GIFT procedure disqualifies it as assistance to the conjugal act since the continuity between the act and fertilization is fractured. In other words, the sheer number of interventions has the cumulative effect of severing the essential link between the marital act and fertilization. These interventions singly considered are: the use of ovulatory drugs, laparoscopic retrieval of eggs, replacement of eggs into the fallopian tubes, collecting semen with a perforated Silastic sheath in a conjugal act, treating the sperm, and injecting semen into the uterus. Interventions that are, when taken singly, considered at least possibly licit, because the actions are understood to preserve the essential link between the conjugal act and conception, become illicit in GIFT because there are too many of them.[83] If certain interventions such as those mentioned above are permissible taken individually, then the objection implies a threshold number which makes the moral difference between assistance and replacement. GIFT exceeds this threshold, which becomes a reason for its rejection.

Responses to the two central objections can be made which, on the one hand, acknowledge that the actions of GIFT do possess a unity of their own and do constitute a series of discrete steps, and on the other, demonstrate that these aspects of the actions are consistent with genuine assistance to the conjugal act. It is true that the various actions and instruments used in the GIFT procedure have a formal nature independent of the conjugal act. The actions, for example, of washing sperm and moving the haploid gametes

[82] How the acts are categorized (either each separately, or subsumed under two main acts, the conjugal act as one and the technical act of GIFT as the other) is irrelevant to the point that their are several discrete acts occurring in GIFT.

[83] See Thomas J. O'Donnell, S.J., *Medicine and Christian Morality* (New York: Alba House, Second Revised and Updated Edition, 1991), 239; Haas, "Gift? No!," 2-3; DeMarco, *Biotechnology and the Assault on Parenthood,* 225-226, 233; Nicholas Tonti-Filippini, "'Donum Vitae' and Gamete Intra-Fallopian Tube Transfer," *Linacre Quarterly,* 57:2 (1990), 74-75.

down a catheter into the fallopian tube can be understood for what they are quite separate from the marital act. The various substances used in sperm preparation for separation of motile spermatozoa or for motility enhancement, and the physical instruments used such as the Silastic sheath or the catheter all possess a nature of their own. But these facts are not inconsistent with the concept of assistance. That which assists is by definition not of a part of the thing which it assists. As the analysis of the relation between principal and instrumental causality showed, the instrumental cause has a specific form or nature and is able to assist the principal cause only by exercising the proper action of its form.

The ontological objection to GIFT, viz., that GIFT replaces the conjugal act because its actions have a unity and intelligibility separate from the act, assumes that anything that assists must in its very unity and intelligibility be of the same nature as that which it assists. But this is circular. The truth of the conclusion that GIFT replaces the conjugal act because the procedure's actions possess their own unity depends upon the truth of the larger assumption, which is the very thing in need of independent proof. The conclusion follows not from independent evidence but from the suppressed assumption. However, the converse of the assumption is the truth. Anything that assists the conjugal act does so only because it is not essentially related to the act. The ontological objection is formulated precisely because the distinction between principal and instrumental causality is not taken into account.

Moreover, the assumption that assistance to the conjugal act must itself be part of the act's unity and intelligibility further implies that anything that is not contiguous with the physical act of coitus cannot rightly be regarded as assisting the act.[84] However, this would wrongly make the causality of the conjugal act equivalent to the physical completion of coitus and would not be consistent with the teaching. As *Donum vitae* indicates, the causality of the conjugal act is not restricted to the physical act of coitus but extends to a natural objective that is other than the coitus itself, and is fulfilled in the meeting of the haploid gametes in fertilization.[85] Thus, anything that is not physically contiguous

---

[84] This in fact is the result for some who make the ontological objection. See Tonti-Filippini, "'Donum Vitae' and GIFT," 70-77; May, "Catholic Teaching," 88; Haas, "Gift? No!," 2-3; DeMarco, *Biotechnology and the Assault on Parenthood*, 208-212 and 226-233; O'Donnell, *Medicine and Christian Morality*, 238.

[85] *Donum vitae*, II, B, 4: the "*conjugal act...is per se suitable for the generation of children....*"; see also II, B, 5-6 on the connection between the conjugal act and procreation.

with coitus itself cannot *ipso facto* be excluded from the category of assistance.

The potential for abuse in the technical actions of GIFT mentioned above is thought to be further evidence of the fact that the actions in GIFT are essentially independent of the conjugal act.[86] While these possibilities do demonstrate that the natures of the actions in GIFT are separate from the essence of the conjugal act, it does not follow that procedures that are physically contiguous to the act do not carry the same potential for abuse, nor does the potential for abuse in and of itself disqualify GIFT as genuine assistance. With respect to the first point, for example, an egg retrieved in LTOT or sperm collected in a cervical spoon could be used with the gametes of someone other than the spouse using IVF or any number of other procedures, or the sperm could be discarded. The potential for abusing the actions in GIFT does not prove anything about the morality of GIFT. Moreover, the potential for abuse is present in virtually all the actions of medicine. The relevant question is not whether any particular action in GIFT can be wrongly used in some cases, but whether GIFT has a morally right use.

The cumulative threshold objection supposes an undefined threshold number of actions beyond which a procedure replaces the marital act. GIFT exceeds this threshold. This objection assumes the result of the ontological objection, viz., that any legitimate assistance must be physically contiguous with the coitus. The greater the number, the less contiguous the individual actions of a procedure are with the coitus, and, therefore, the more fertilization is due to the technical actions. If it is assumed that the proper causality of the conjugal act is direct, without any intervening causes between it and fertilization, then from a moral point of view the fewer and more contiguous the interventions of a procedure, the better. However, no cause, save the one First Cause, acts independently of other causes. The coordinate activity of the spouses in the conjugal act, like all other finite causal action, depends upon other causes for its being. This is why all created causes are known as secondary causes. The unity of the sex act necessarily represents an intrinsic structure of secondary causes intervening between the conjugal act and its effect, fertilization. Thus, it would be inaccurate to criticize GIFT on the basis that it

[86] See, for example, May, "Pastoral Concerns," 167; DeMarco, *Biotechnology and the Assault on Parenthood,* 227.

does not meet an assumed standard of direct causality in which the effect of fertilization is directly dependent upon the single conjugal act of the spouses.[87]

It seems that the notion of a threshold is incompatible with the attempt to distinguish assistance from replacement, given the nature of assistance. What is the threshold number assumed in this objection, and how could it be determined? If it is true that GIFT disrupts the natural causal chain, then all attempts at assisting the conjugal act are *per se* illicit. Any assistance to the marital act, by definition, reduces the natural dimension. Even the LTOT procedure or the use of a cervical spoon to move semen across some physiological barrier alters in several ways the natural process between conjugal act and fertilization. Assistance is unavoidably disruptive. Moreover, *Donum vitae* does not place an inherent, quantitative limit to the concept of assistance. The question is not over the number of steps or whether each occurs as one discrete event at a time, for these are aspects of any assistance. Rather, the question is whether the disruption is such that it replaces the principal causality of the conjugal act by replacing the causal factors immediate to fertilization itself, thereby severing the intrinsic link between marital coitus and new life.

Conclusion

The teaching of *Gaudium et spes* on contraception quoted earlier is directly relevant to the topic of reproductive technologies. It indicates that the ordination of marriage to procreation must be accomplished in and through conjugal love:

> [W]hen there is question of harmonizing married love with the responsible transmission of life, it is not enough to take only the good intention and the evaluation of motives into account; the objective criteria must be used, criteria drawn from the nature of the human person and human action, criteria which respect the total meaning of mutual self-giving and human procreation in the context of true love; all this is possible only if the virtue of married chastity is seriously practiced.[88]

---

[87] See Tonti-Filippini, "'Donum Vitae' and GIFT," 70-75; May, "Catholic Teaching," 88; DeMarco, *Biotechnology and the Assault on Parenthood,* 226.

[88] "*Ubi de componendo amore coniugali cum responsabili vitae transmissione agitur, non a sola sincera intentione et aestimatione motivorum pendet, sed obiectivis criteriis, ex personae eiusdemque actuum natura desumptis, determinari debet, quae integrum sensum mutuae donationis ac humanae procreationis in contextu veri amoris observant; quod fieri nequit nisi virtus castitatis coniugalis*

That conjugal chastity to which *Gaudium et spes* refers applies not only to preserving the inseparable connection between the unitive and procreative meanings of the conjugal act in the avoidance of pregnancy, but applies also to procreation. In this way the offspring of the spouses' actions may be the fruit of a true union—a union in which the spouses give all that they are as man and woman to each other. If it is otherwise, the actions of the spouses will not be truly unitive even though donor gametes or surrogacy are not used, and neither will their actions be truly procreative even though a child has been produced. As increasingly more new techniques for infertility intervention are developed and the identification of procedures that assist as distinct from those that replace the conjugal act becomes increasingly less clear, the challenge of applying Church teaching in this area will grow in proportion. The key, I believe, to meeting this challenge is to use a criterion that begins retrospectively from the act of fertilization itself, and determines whether the various immediate causal factors of fertilization are principally caused by the conjugal act, though aided by instrumental causes and active conditions.

The metaphysical argument and the criterion for judging specific reproductive technologies presented here are to be understood as theological opinion. With respect to GIFT, given that theologians and philosophers in accord with the Magisterium have expressed opinions both in favor of it and against it, and given the absence of a specific magisterial pronouncement on it, Catholics may, according to a rightly informed conscience, licitly choose it. If the Magisterium should teach that GIFT is morally wrong and impermissible, I will happily retract the affected opinions, and will support and defend the teaching without reservation.

sincero animo colatur" (*Gaudium et spes*, 51).

CHAPTER 7

Catholic Health Care: Justice, Fiscal Realities, and Moral Norms

JOSEPH J. PICCIONE, J.D.

Catholic health care services were established in the United States before the nation achieved its independence, and over the course of years has developed from nursing care to advanced integrated delivery systems of care. The members of religious communities who founded these apostolic endeavors served their original communities, and expanded to meet new needs; they heeded the call to serve in the Civil War, in times of epidemic, and always the poor and marginalized. Speaking to Catholic health care leaders at a 1987 assembly in Phoenix, Arizona, Pope John Paul II stated:

> Your healthcare ministry, pioneered and developed by congregations of women religious and by congregations of brothers, is one of the most vital apostolates of the ecclesiastical community and one of the most significant services which the Catholic Church offers to society in the name of Jesus Christ.[1]

[1] "Address to the Catholic Health Care Ministry," Phoenix, September 14, 1987.

Health care represents a fundamental good, and the caring response to health needs—interventions to sustain health, to assist in recovery, or to provide the solidarity of care when cure is not possible—witnesses to the truth about the human person. In the same address the Holy Father told the group: "Because of your dedication to caring for the sick and the poor, the aged and the dying, you know from your own daily experience how much illness and suffering are basic problems of human existence."[2] This care is a sign of the Kingdom of God and confirms the identity of the Church, in her discipleship to Jesus, who cared for those who were afflicted by sickness. The health care ministry is a mission the Church has received from her divine founder, and is a manifestation of the civilization of love. As such, the Church has a moral right to continue in the health care ministry, and to show her enduring concern for persons and for civilization. Health care is now undergoing a period of restructuring in the United States that presents a range of new challenges to the Catholic health care mission. This paper will address health care restructuring and the emerging issues of morality, justice, and finance.

A Time of Reconfiguration in Health Care in the United States

"Health care in the United States is marked by extraordinary change."[3] This first sentence of the Preamble to the current *Ethical and Religious Directives* is a very appropriate one indeed. The Preamble notes the clinical advances that mark contemporary health care, these constant changes which we often take for granted. More striking, however, is the truly "extraordinary change" evidenced by a new role played by payers of health care services, namely, employers, who seek greater cost control without sacrificing quality of care. Specifically on the national legislative and policy levels, there is a reexamination of the structure of programs representing long-standing commitments to provide necessary medical services to the poor and the aged. Finally, there are significant, but long-developing shifts within the religious congregations of men and women who have sponsored Catholic health care services, some representing commitments of more than a century and a half to their communities. Fewer religious are

---

[2] Ibid.

[3] National Conference of Catholic Bishops, *Ethical and Religious Directives for Catholic Health Care Services*, approved November 1994, published March 1995.

available in facilities, where once there was a sister in each unit every shift, who represented both Christian charity and the religious identity of the institution. Consequently, more of the Catholic laity and other Christians share responsibility for the mission with their religious sponsors.

New relationships have also characterized this restructuring process. These new alliances and sometimes, partnerships, among health care providers are truly phenomenal when we consider that a decade ago, these providers often saw themselves as completely distinct from other professionals or institutions. Where in the recent past, a stand-alone hospital was seen as normative, today and in the future, a stand-alone hospital without other provider or network linkages, can be viewed as being in a most precarious position. The previous stand-alone hospital model permitted the Catholic institution to avoid any relationship with morally objectionable services or with other institutions that offered these services. The evolving health care model is one that, simply put, does not afford the Catholic entity the same degree of control of the health care environment. Rather than a series of unrelated acute care facilities, health care provision is becoming more an "ecosystem" of providers and relationships. Catholic institutions must negotiate this new reality very carefully, yet expeditiously.

Federal government funding patterns will shift and present a major impact on health care provision. Government funding is found in a range of programs assisting health care providers: indirect funding which appears as state programs; or social insurance programs, such as Medicare and Medicaid. These appropriations, in short, affect everything in health care, and any modification, even those to save the long-term prospects of the programs, are viewed with great concern by providers.

In short, the health care sector of American life, which has enjoyed tremendous growth and stability for decades, is now a very worried group of institutions and professionals.

Greater Challenges to Catholic Providers

These changing realities are recognized in the 1994 *Ethical and Religious Directives.* For all the concerns that secular health care providers have about their future survival and well-being, Catholic providers have greater concerns, and greater peril is presented to our service.

Catholic health care is not exempt from the restructuring of health care in the United States. If the Church is to continue in the health care ministry, it certainly must take account of the trends in American health care structure and financing, but must be primarily concerned with continuing as a specifically Catholic apostolic endeavor.

This apostolate is one that is prompted by a recognition of the truth of the human person, beginning with the insight of the vulnerability of the sick person and completed by Divine Revelation—this vulnerable person is sacred and bears the image of God. The virtues of justice and charity characterize our response to those we serve.

Justice affirms that health care is a fundamental human good, and all persons possess a moral right to adequate health care. Justice also affirms that human life is to be protected at all its stages from conception to natural death and that "particular attention should be given to the health care needs of the poor, the uninsured and the underinsured."[4]

The theological virtue of charity gives the particular character to Christian health care services. The gift of the grace of God enables us to love others as God loves them, and is the basis of the many charisms of service to the human person, especially to the poor in body or spirit. Pope Saint Leo the Great wrote:

> No act of devotion on the part of the faithful gives God more pleasure than that which is lavished on His poor. Where He finds charity with its loving concern, there He recognizes the reflection of His own fatherly care. (Tuesday, Week IV of Lent, Office of Readings)

In his recent encyclical, *The Gospel of Life*, Pope John Paul II describes qualities necessary in the health care ministry to life at all its stages:

> In our service of charity, *we must be inspired and distinguished by a specific attitude:* we must care for the other as a person for whom God has made us responsible. As disciples of Jesus, we are called to become neighbors to everyone (cf. *Lk* 10:29-37), and to show special favor to those who are poorest, most alone and most in need. In helping the hungry, the thirsty, the foreigner, the naked, the sick, the imprisoned—as well as the child in the womb and the old person who is suffering or

---

[4] Ibid., Introduction to Part One.

near death—we have the opportunity to serve Jesus. He himself said: "As you did it to one of the least of these my brethren, you did it to me" (*Mt* 25:40).[5]

We can see how the founders and foundresses of Catholic health care services in the United States were motivated by this vision, and their words and example show us the path to follow.

Pope John Paul II in *The Gospel of Life* provides a vision of this linkage between the truth of the human person, justice, and charity. After an analysis of the ethical relativism to which cultural debate is prone today, the Holy Father narrates the significance of moral norms, valid always and everywhere. These norms, even in their negative formulation, have a special significance for human freedom. The Pope writes:

> In this sense, the negative moral precepts have an extremely important positive function. The "no" which they unconditionally require makes clear the absolute limit beneath which free individuals cannot lower themselves. At the same time they indicate the minimum which they must respect and from which they must start out in order to say "yes" over and over again, a "yes" which will gradually embrace the *entire horizon of the good* (cf. *Mt* 5:48). (*EV*, 75)

In his concern for contemporary persons, the Holy Father warns that a pluralist society may seek a type of social peace by the practice of ethical relativism. But such an approach cannot be genuine or long lasting. When the truth of the moral "no" for the sake of the moral "yes" is clearly stated, this continuing cultural debate about moral norms, and ultimately, a dispute about the nature of the human person will necessarily be joined once more.

Growth, Challenges, and Fundamental Standards in Catholic Health Care in the United States

In a number of recent addresses and papers, Cardinal Joseph Bernardin has discussed the development of Catholic health care in the United States in an era in which great clinical advances were taking place. This period of growth offered Catholic providers the opportunity to remain in step and grow with these clinical advances. At this time in the United States, Catholic providers

---

[5] Pope John Paul II, *Evangelium vitae* (March 25, 1995), 87 (hereafter cited in the body of the text as *EV* with section numbers).

represent about 10 percent of the nation's non-federal hospitals, and are the largest grouping of not-for-profit providers, caring for 64 million persons as inpatients or outpatients in 1994—very impressive indeed for a religion that was often a scorned minority in the early decades of this century. This growth brought with it the perils of being in the world, but not of the world. As our services expanded in clinical depth and breadth of scope, we could sometimes act like businesses, in fact, very important businesses and major employers in our communities.

How we act and how we appear are areas of continuing concern for Catholic health care. Catholic health care institutions grew because they were based on the Lord's command of charitable service, and the Church's charter of religious communities and their mandate to serve persons and the health care needs. Even in areas in which Catholicism is a minority religion, they are accepted because these communities perceive that the service rendered is based on a religious mission of the institution providing care but not on the religious affiliation of the person receiving care. And at the heart of the founders of these religious communities and missions was always the desire to serve the poor in body and spirit. This, too, has always been recognized as a distinctive quality of Catholic health care. And these communities and their lay associates very much want to continue their service to the poor and underserved, as health care is transformed.

Service to the poor and marginalized is intrinsic to the definition of Catholic health care. One significant threat to this service arises from the sheer enormity of the cost of provision of sophisticated health care services. To digress slightly but for a good reason: the business principles utilized by the Catholic provider must be sound, but ultimately not for the business end of profitability for investors. We are not a business or an industry (and must avoid that language), but a ministry of service; our use of business principles must be for the sake of our *stewardship* of resources. A second difficulty arising for Catholic providers in the restructuring of health care is that of financing services for the poor by the federal government: The national government has long been a source of some, if often inadequate or delayed, funding for services for these persons.

As national leaders struggle to put the financing of these services on a more solid basis, a shift to capitated or managed care is underway, already existing experimentally in some states. While a managed care approach can be structured for provision of quality services, future Medicaid services for low-income persons will probably be oriented to young women and their children, and will include the full range of services intended by the legislators, both those that are morally sound and those procedures that are immoral. The instinct of the Catholic provider is to serve the poor, yet our concern to meet the needs of the underserved cannot exclude Catholic moral norms, otherwise we would formally cooperate with, or even do evil for the sake of other goods. The charitable instinct is not served by performing services that are not truly charitable, denying the dignity of the human person, marriage, or life itself. Catholic health care cannot provide morally objectionable services as if health care were simply a commodity, driven by market needs, or state mandate.

This example of a list of mandated services is one further example of the ongoing debate on the meaning of the human person. Catholic health care is again on the front lines of this dispute. We must neither put aside our recognition of the truths of human life, nor defer the proclamation of the good news of human life to meet the expectations of the state and its lists of procedures that must be included if we are to continue our service to the poor. At the present time, no definitive list of mandated services is available; in fact, such determination may be left to the states. Also at this time, there is no grave threat that abortion services will be included in a list of minimum services defined by the federal government. However, a range of family planning services including contraceptive sterilization is more likely to appear in the state plans, and planning for these eventualities is underway in Catholic health care providers in dioceses across the nation, because serving the poor is intrinsic to the definition of Catholic health care.

Another challenge to the health care apostolate arises from the growth of the phenomenon of purely for-profit health care provision. Health care is a key social and economic sector in contemporary life, and the not-for-profit providers now find that they are far from alone in their willingness to serve specific areas. A fundamental distinction should be seen between these two types of providers. The for-profit entity addresses the needs of a particular "market" and ultimately must justify its performance to investors. The not-for-profit entity certainly strives for financial stability to continue its work, but regards its areas of practice not as marketplaces but as service areas, and attempts to weather times of unprofitability in a particular service area by shifting resources from other sites. The not-for-profits, as Cardinal Bernardin has written, include hospitals with religious sponsorship as well as community hospitals. They, despite religious differences, have much more in common with each other than they have with the for-profits. All the not-for-profits tend to see their activities as a continuation of the unique professional-patient relationship, and are influenced by the core values of this relationship. They see health care as a profession of service, with the central value of service of the human person, a service of beneficence. The for-profit approach, on the other hand, appears happy to describe itself as a business, and to regard its technically correct services as commodities.

Particular challenges flow from this: both external and internal issues. The external issues presented are the maintenance of the religious or not-for-profit mission in the face of the emergence of growing networks of for-profit providers, some of which will represent enormous financial resources. The stakes are high in this challenge: the Catholic health care presence can be seriously threatened by this movement, as can the very future of the health care profession and the professional-patient relationship. In restating the meaning of the profession, Catholic health care has an opportunity to witness these values to the American public.

There is an internal challenge as well: as Catholic health care leaders, many of whom are laypersons, regard the success of the for-profits, we may see some emulation of this business approach. Certainly we should utilize the skills presented for good and efficient stewardship of our resources, but must resist the model of corporate life and corporate culture.

Consideration of this internal challenge is important: If we talk like business leaders and think like business leaders and structure personal rewards like business leaders, we will not be effective models of the ministry of service. As laypersons take the leadership roles of religious sisters and brothers, the laity must understand that they, too, are now the symbols of this service, and their concerns for the conduct of the service must extend beyond financial performance.

There is a rather common expression in the not-for-profit health care sector: "No margin, no mission." The best response I

102

have heard to that was from a religious sister health care director who replied, "No mission, no margin." We exist because of our mission of service; stewardship keeps us cognizant of fiscal realities, but these are not the sole realities for us. The other realities are, of course, moral norms and the virtues of justice and charity.

Thus, the corporate culture is a critical area in health care. The Franciscan sisters of OSF Healthcare System developed a "Ministry Development Program" for administrators and key managers. In the course of a five-year period, more than 800 persons have completed the first level of three two-day meetings in a retreat house with annual renewal sessions. It is appropriate that those who are entrusted with the operation of an apostolate of the Church understand the mission and vision that drives this service. This is a very significant program for OSF Healthcare, because it helps us to build the health care of tomorrow on the foundation established by our pioneer sisters. This program helps managers operationalize the organization's value statement, and reminds them of their common accountability for the stewardship of the mission. Around the health care system, the various facilities also conduct programs for all employees in the local site, to propagate the common mission and vision.

The *Ethical and Religious Directives* address the restructuring of health care and can assist in shaping the Catholic institution's internal culture. For many of us, the era of the stand-alone hospital has already passed. In this new era of complex and challenging relationships, assistance and guidance is necessary for lay leaders of Catholic health care. For many of us, the previous experience of the stand-alone hospital, in which the Catholic sponsor is entirely free to exclude any contact or involvement with other providers who may offer morally objectionable services, is not always the case in the present. This will be increasingly common in the restructuring of health care, and assistance is necessary for lay leaders of Catholic health care, who are under tremendous pressure to guide these services through a challenging period and maintain financial viability. Included in this pressure will be forces from health care payers to go beyond the established norms of cooperation for the sake of survival. These leaders were used to the past era when no linkages to morally objectionable services were even entertained. In this rapidly unfolding evolutionary period, leaders are being introduced to the classical moral concept of *cooperation*, applied to the legal person of the corporation.

But *cooperation* is not a blanket expression, suddenly permitting previously prohibited involvement. It is a discernment of the situation that could permit a remote material cooperation, and an avoidance of both immediate material cooperation and formal cooperation, which are impermissible. In cooperation issues, there are fundamental distinctions that must be understood before they can be applied. And there are dramatic polarities of meaning; remote material and formal cooperation have very real differences. These meanings are not purely distinguished by the intention, wish, or hope of the entity at question; it is in fact all too easy to slip from material to formal cooperation. Any resulting erosion of the integrity of the Catholic provider will be most difficult to reconstruct. Yes, this is a perilous time for Catholic health care.

Practical Considerations:
Catholic Collaboration; the Importance of Bishops in Assuring the Integrity of Catholic Health Care; Hopes for the Future

As it is remarkable that the once stand-alone hospitals have been developing alliances with other providers, it is also remarkable that Catholic providers are actually developing alliances and sometimes mergers with other Catholic providers. Certainly, one would think that entities with a common mission from the Church, common values relative to health care, concern for the poor, and the sacredness of human life would naturally collaborate. But collaboration also requires a common vision of what the future may look like, and the steps necessary to move into the future. Collaboration among Catholic providers can arise from a new perspective of the charism of religious communities that sponsor facilities in a particular diocese or region. As sponsors regard the charism of their health care ministry as a mission shared with other Catholic sponsors, it becomes possible to overcome previous absolute separations between religious communities, and meet the challenges of regional and state health care restructuring. Of course, it is appropriate for local bishops and state Catholic conferences to participate in this discernment and foster collaboration among Catholic services. These affiliation issues present additional concerns for Catholic health care integrity; Catholic sponsors should prioritize exploration and development of meaningful collaborative relationships with other Catholic

104

services as a necessary step before cooperative ventures with other than Catholic providers.

In addition to planning the design of the future of health care services, Catholic providers and the national and state Catholic conferences should also collaborate in addressing the possibility of morally objectionable services being mandated by federal and state legislators. They must work together to gain necessary conscience protection in federal and state legislation. Certainly many conscience clauses exist in legislation; particular conscience protection may provide protection for *providers*, but such would not protect Catholic-sponsored networks or HMOs, which are not legally defined as providers of services. Such a clause should be very broad in scope. Still, in practice, specific instances may require remote material cooperation in some morally objectionable services, but such would be controlled by the Catholic entity and not the state or "the market." Although contemporary America will not understand or agree with our conscience concerns, a society that claims to be "pluralist" should be required to respect our conscientious objections. No legislature should hold Catholic providers hostage by requiring provision of immoral services as a condition to caring for the needs of the poor, but immoral services will be included in definitions of required services for Medicaid recipients.

Hope arises from one bill: the *Medical Training Non-Discrimination Act of 1995* passed in the House of Representatives (H.R. 1932) but stalled in the Senate (S. 971). This would prohibit a governmental entity from discriminating against health professionals who refuse to undergo or provide training in induced abortions. This bill was drafted with the assistance of the Pro-Life Secretariat of the NCCB. If successful, this will give new protection to Catholic medical schools and pro-life medical students and physicians. It is an example of the type of legislation so needed by Catholic providers.

Development of more complete conscience clause protection is a useful defensive strategy for the integrity of Catholic health care. Pursuit of this does not entail abandonment of the proactive strategy of eliminating unethical and inhuman elements from future legislation. These strategies complement each other, and should be seen in this light.

These legislative struggles remind us of the continuing, underlying cultural dispute about the nature of the human person and with it the nature of the health care profession, in service to the

105

human person. Health care can reaffirm the significance of the traditional personal relationship, or shift to a new identity as a technical dispenser of a commodity. Health care is a noble profession. Pope John Paul II summoned the American church, and we should hear this call in Catholic health care, too, in his homily at Camden Yards in Baltimore:

> Sometimes, witnessing to Christ will mean drawing out of a culture the full meaning of its noblest intentions, a fullness that is revealed in Christ. At other times, witnessing to Christ means challenging that culture, especially when the truth about the human person is under assault.[6]

This is a unique time, and presents dramatic challenges to the identity and integrity of Catholic health care. For years, the pastoral responsibility of the bishops in health care could largely be exercised by addressing Catholic providers themselves; but at this time of health care transformation, the bishops, in national and state conferences may find the pastoral necessity to publicly address legislators on these pressing issues. Due to the peril facing the integrity of Catholic health care, the conferences can examine their strategies and tactics, and draw a bright line of demarcation which would demonstrate that Catholic providers can have no involvement in direct actions against human life.

The recent *Ethical and Religious Directives* has been helpful in addressing Catholic providers; at this key juncture the bishops can take that same message to the public and legislators. The practical result of this can be to substantially affect the dynamics of this transformation and to provide a basis of consistency for Catholic health care leaders who are grappling with commercial and political demands. At present, consistency in application is sorely needed, yet somwhat elusive.

In responding to the needs of the health care apostolate, American bishops have developed new resources. Increasingly, bishops are designating health care liaisons or ethicists to represent them in the discernment and implementation processes necessary for cooperation cases. OSF Healthcare has its corporate office in Peoria, Illinois; our bishop has designated a vicar for health care ethics, with whom we reflect on the transformation of health care and the challenges to Catholic health care ministry in the diocese. Rockford, Illinois, is also one of our service areas, and the local

---

[6] Homily at Camden Yards, Baltimore, October 8, 1995.

bishop also has designated a diocesan ethicist for health care issues. The Peoria diocese also has developed a document process that must be completed and submitted to the health care vicar for evaluation prior to any alliance or joint venture in which Catholic identity or integrity could be jeopardized; this is similar to the protocol developed by Cardinal Bernardin in Chicago. And in the Diocese of Peoria there is another document that must be completed annually to review the necessity of the arrangement as well as the status of educational efforts regarding the implementation.

Health care and the people in health care are about hope: certainly a hope that through skilled intervention, health can be maintained or restored, or hope that when cure is not possible, patients will understand the value they represent and the love God has for them. This hope is coupled with the belief that the configuration of health care services will be redesigned to provide more effective interventions. For example, instead of meeting acute care needs, we will have the opportunity to redesign care, with opportunities to work with diocesan Catholic Social Services, to meet needs in light of the truth of the human person. This is what keeps us going at a time of great anxiety.

Justice, charity, and hope are the foundation and legacy of Catholic health care in its response to the truth of the human person. We are charged, at this time of crisis, to preserve what has been entrusted to us, and to engage the challenges of the future.

Finally, future challenges will be more than institutional survival: we are recommitting ourselves to this service of charity, and to the nobility of the human person, and we know that this will engage us even more deeply in the question of the human person. The fourth and final chapter of *The Gospel of Life* is both an inspiring and joyous affirmation of life, and our cultural obligations:

> What is urgently called for is a *general mobilization of consciences* and a *united ethical effort* to activate a *great campaign in support of life. All together, we must build a new culture of life:* new, because it will be able to confront and solve today's unprecedented problems affecting human life; new, because it will be adopted with deeper and more dynamic conviction by all Christians; new, because it will be capable of bringing about a serious and courageous cultural dialogue among all parties. While the urgent need for such a cultural transformation is linked to the present historical situation, it

is also rooted in the Church's mission of evangelization. The purpose of the Gospel, in fact, is "to transform humanity from within and to make it new".[7] (*EV*, 95)

[7] Paul VI, Apostolic Exhortation *Evangelii nuntiandi* (December 8, 1975), 18: *AAS* 68 (1976), 17.

CHAPTER 8

Ethical Quandary: Forming Hospital Partnerships

THE REVEREND RUSSELL E. SMITH, S.T.D.

Introduction

In the past three years, one of the most common consultation requests submitted to the Pope John Center has been for assistance in the ethical assessment of proposed hospital partnerships between Catholic and non-Catholic providers. When preparing for a lecture on the application of the principles of cooperation to health care alliances last year for the Fourteenth Bishops' Workshop, there were virtually no contemporary sources to turn to. Theologians had not yet published articles on the topic, although many of us were actively engaged in working with Catholic health care sponsors and administrators on this precise question. Religious congregations generally had "in house" documents for boards and administrators to use as guides in compatibility studies and approval protocols. In the last twelve months, however, a number of articles have appeared.

This essay, presented at the Fifteenth Bishops' Workshop (February 1996) for the purposes of inclusion in this volume, was first printed in *Linacre Quarterly*, vol. 63, no. 2 (May 1995), 87-96. It appears here with minor revisions and corrections.

Among them, there are two very thoughtful and thought-provoking articles from two distinguished Catholic ethicists. The first, by Father Richard McCormick, entitled "The Catholic Hospital Today: Mission Impossible?" focuses on the broad spectrum of changes in the delivery of health care and the practice of medicine, which have dramatically altered both the culture of the hospital and the culture of the doctor-patient relationship.[1] McCormick describes eight characteristics that form a context of health care different than that present in the first half of this century: the depersonalization that results from medical technology and efficiency; the secularization of the medical profession (understood as "increasing preoccupation with factors that are peripheral to and distractive from holistic human care [like] competition, liability, government controls, finances"[2]); a contrast emerging in the medical ethos from focus on the ethics of individual clinical decisions to concern for broader social and economic concerns; the market-driven health care system; the death-denying technological imperative resulting in over treatment; continued fascination with high-tech rescue medicine; an increasingly disembodied understanding of health and disease; and the need for fewer acute care hospitals. As a result of these developments, he says, "We see a Catholic hospital questioning its identity" and "[T]here is a gap between institutional purpose and aim, and personal conviction and involvement"[3] on the part of Catholics involved in this work. He summarizes this as follows:

> We see people who have jobs, not great causes.
>
> I think this may well have happened to many Catholic hospitals. They were organized around the "greatest story ever told."...The Catholic hospital exists, therefore, to be Jesus' love for the other in the health care setting. It has the daily vocation of telling every patient—especially the poor—and every employee how great they are, because Jesus told us how great we are and in the process empowered us. Yet I suspect this raison d'etre has become practically dysfunctional. If that is the case, then the heart of the Catholic health care culture is gone. The mission has become impossible.[4]

[1] Richard McCormick, S.J., "The Catholic Hospital Today: Mission Impossible?" *Origins*, vol. 24, no. 39 (March 16, 1995), 648-653.

[2] Ibid., 650.

[3] Ibid., 649 and 648, respectively.

[4] Ibid., 649.

Father McCormick ends his talk with the question of whether the "soul" of Catholic hospitals can be saved in light of the necessary elements of Catholic identity and a health care setting hostile to those elements.

The second distinguished Catholic ethicist, Professor Germain Grisez, answers Father McCormick's question in the negative.[5] Professor Grisez focuses his attention precisely on the principles of cooperation. He maintains much of the involvement of Catholic institutions in the evolution of health care delivery is formal cooperation and that which is material cooperation should not be permitted either. This position will be addressed later, but I mention it here as one concrete answer to the fundamental question articulated by Father McCormick, an answer that contrasts sharply with the opinion of Catholic sponsors, the Church's pastoral leadership, and the Catholic Health Association (CHA).

CHA has collaborated with the National Coalition on Catholic Health Care Ministry to produce a workbook that is actually a dossier of items to provide assistance to everyone studying the question of the Church's continued involvement in health care.[6] It is a collection of articles, charts, suggested models, and graphs aimed at explaining how and why Catholic sponsors can remain in this ministry. This coalition answers "yes" to Father McCormick's question. In this essay I would like to add to this conversation by examining the "no" and "yes" sides of the answer. Specifically, I will review the conclusions of my essay of last year on cooperation in health care alliances,[7] clarify some ambiguous concepts by defining "duress," "scandal," and "immediate material cooperation," and address a few aspects of general application to health care alliances and our relationships with physicians.

---

[5] Germain Grisez, "Difficult Moral Questions: How Far May Catholic Hospitals Cooperate with Non-Catholic Providers?" *Linacre Quarterly*, vol. 62, no. 4, (November, 1995) 67-72.

[6] *Catholic Health Ministry in Transition: A Handbook for Responsible Leadership* (Silver Spring, Md.: National Coalition on Catholic Health Care Ministry, 1995).

[7] Russell E. Smith, "The Principles of Cooperation and Their Application to the Present State of Health Care Evolution," in *The Splendor of Truth and Health Care: Proceedings of the Fourteenth Workshop for Bishops* (Braintree, Mass.: Pope John Center, 1995), 217-231. A slightly modified version of this essay also appeared in *Catholic Health Ministry in Transition* (see previous footnote).

The Principles of Cooperation

The first intervention of the Magisterium in the field of morals occurred in 1679 when Pope Innocent XI–through the agency of the Inquisition–condemned sixty-five theses of moral doctrine as being laxist. Number 51 is a laxist rendering of the sinfulness of a certain kind of cooperation: the case of a servant carrying a ladder or opening the window of his master to facilitate the master's rape of a woman.[8] While this example sounds archaic and I would never suggest that you use this as an example at a hospital board meeting unless you like being laughed at, we will return to it later in this presentation.

It would take almost a century to articulate a coherent understanding of cooperation that was considered neither lax nor rigorist. This development would be fundamentally the work of St. Alphonsus Liguori. He made the principles of cooperation acceptable by introducing the distinction between formal and material cooperation (the former never acceptable, while certain forms of the latter could possibly be acceptable) and by considering scandal as a serious invitation to sin. Cooperation in the ethically significant sense is defined as the participation of one agent in the activity of another agent to produce a particular effect or joint activity. This becomes ethically problematical when the action of the primary agent is morally wrong.

The fundamental distinction is that between formal and material cooperation. Formal cooperation involves willing participation in an intrinsically evil act. Material cooperation is either immediate or mediate. I will discuss immediate material cooperation later in the essay. Mediate material cooperation is proximate or remote, free or necessary. Mediate material cooperation can be justified if there is a significant reason to engage in the proposed course of action and if scandal can be avoided.

Needless to say, a determination that a proposed partnership is mediate material cooperation is not the same as saying such a proposal is prudent. There may be local, particular factors which complicate such an enterprise and which the principles, baldly stated, would be blind to. In general, however, there are four basic theological and pastoral concerns that must be addressed. First, the extent and type of cooperation entailed in the partnership

---

[8] H. Denzinger and A. Schonmetzer, *Enchiridion Symbolorum*, 36th ed., (Barcinone: Herder, 1976), 2151. See Russell E. Smith, "The Principles of Cooperation."

should be fleshed out. Second, cooperation with partners who perform some activities we deem morally inappropriate must derive from some "serious reason." The pressures of health care delivery evolution can be this serious reason. Third, the potential for scandal—and the potential for notoriety—have to be looked at. And fourth, the canonical questions of sponsorship and alienation of property require serious attention. This is particularly acute today because our experience of the relationship of *ownership*, *control*, and *sponsorship* is changing. In some cases, for example, it has been suggested that the *sponsor* sell its hospital (relinquishing *ownership*), but that the *sponsor* can retain *control* of the hospital through contractual agreements that would respect those essential ingredients of reserved powers that canonical stewards must exercise to maintain Catholic identity, such as establishment of philosophy and mission, the further disposition of the assets, closure of the hospital, etc.

There are five basic principles the Pope John Center is using as guidelines in moral evaluations of partnerships:

1. Cooperation must be mediate material, never formal or immediate material.
2. We can only do together what all partners agree to be appropriate. This means that while the alliance or collaborative effort need not be Catholic, it must nevertheless observe the *Ethical and Religious Directives* as respecting the "corporate conscience" of the Catholic partner.
3. Morally illicit procedures cannot be provided on the Catholic campus.
4. Any morally illicit procedure(s) provided on campuses of non-Catholic alliance partners must be excluded from the new alliance corporation through separate incorporation and separate billing mechanisms.
5. All publicity should be straightforward regarding: (a) the need to form an alliance for survival of the apostolate; (b) the good achieved by "rationalizing" health care (the cost-driving reality of competition); (c) the exclusion of immoral procedures from the partnership (while these services will still be available on the campuses of some partner[s]); and (d) the necessity of this publicity appearing also in the promotional literature of the Catholic hospital.

Let us return to Professor Grisez's "no" to health care alliances. He says,

> [I]t seems to me that limited material cooperation is most likely to be morally acceptable in simple contractual arrangements for sharing equipment and physical facilities. I very much doubt that a Catholic hospital can justifiably engage in the material cooperation required by an integrated delivery network or cooperatively operated health maintenance organization.[9]

He thinks that the creation of an integrated delivery network (IDN) or health maintenance organization (HMO) constitutes formal cooperation because:

> In agreeing on this way of providing a full range of services...the Catholic negotiators will have intended that the excluded services be supplied by others under the conditions agreed upon, and that intention will constitute formal cooperation.[10]

This is a serious charge. Professor Grisez is implying that the "moral object" of collaboration includes, at least implicitly, an intention of providing prohibited services. He continues:

> Material cooperation also can be wrong, and a Catholic hospital's material cooperation with the provision of morally unacceptable services is likely to be wrong. Catholic hospitals that avoid wrongful material cooperation and maintain their identity may not be economically viable. Therefore, Catholics committed to health care as an apostolate should look for more suitable ways of carrying it on.[11]

However, there seems to be another way to understand this collaboration. In my opinion, the negotiation involves the intention of the Catholic partner to continue to provide health care within the reconfigured arena and that deliberation about prohibited services is aimed precisely at removing the Catholic partner from involvement with prohibited services. It is tantamount to saying, "We are only going to do together what all

[9] Grisez, "Difficult Moral Questions," 71.
[10] Ibid., 70.
[11] Ibid., 68-69.

114

partners agree is appropriate and anything deemed inappropriate must be the private project of that proponent." This involves the "carve-outs" that give so much meaning and enjoyment to the lives of hospital attorneys. This entails a form of collaboration with other providers by which the Catholic partner is removed entirely from any contact with prohibited services, thereby arguably rendering cooperation *with those services* virtually nil.

The term "prohibited services" covers a wide spectrum of procedures, ranging in ethical seriousness from tubal ligation to abortion (and perhaps euthanasia), none of which can be offered by Catholic providers because of their intrinsically evil nature. But we must not lose sight of the fact that the difference in the respective degrees of seriousness is vast. That is why compatibility studies focus more on sterilization than abortion. Notorious abortion providers are generally excluded from consideration of collaboration early on. And when there is such serious consideration, many more alarms have to be addressed than when abortion is off the table. The National Conference of Catholic Bishops (NCCB) recognizes this distinction in its *Commentary on the Reply of the Sacred Congregation for the Doctrine of the Faith on Sterilization in Catholic Hospitals*[12] and in the *Ethical and Religious Directives.* The "serious reason" allowing material cooperation in the case of providers of contraceptive services is not of the same magnitude as that in the case of providers of abortion services.

Having said this, there is one other very important point that Professor Grisez mentions:

> A Catholic institution's significant, obvious, voluntary cooperation in wrongdoing inevitably will impair or even negate its capacity to provide credible witness....For those engaged in health care as an apostolate to impair their witness so greatly would be utterly self-defeating, since...the essence of apostolate is, not only to bring about a human good such as health, but to practice Christian love and bear witness to the gospel's truth, including love for the tiniest of Jesus' sisters and brothers and truth about injustice toward them.[13]

---

[12] The *Reply of the Sacred Congregation for the Doctrine of the Faith on Sterilization in Catholic Hospitals* was published March 13, 1975; The National Conference of Catholic Bishops, Committee on Doctrine, published its *Commentary* on September 15, 1977. Both documents appear in Publication No. B-127 (Washington, D.C.: United States Catholic Conference, 1983).

[13] Grisez, "Difficult Moral Questions," 71.

Certainly, if involvement in prohibited procedures is formal, this contradiction is an actuality. Evil can never be done even for the sake of otherwise doing great good. Even if cooperation is material, such a contradiction could be implied or perceived. This is the issue of scandal which will be addressed below. However, it seems that cooperation need not be formal for the reasons mentioned above. And it must be stated that even if cooperation remains material, collaboration may be counterindicated for reasons of insurmountable scandal or other pastoral concerns. But these concerns lie in the realm of prudential decision, not moral principle.

Three Troublesome Ambiguities

At this juncture, I would like to address briefly three concepts that are used often whose meaning is implied rather than specified: scandal, immediate material cooperation, and duress.

Scandal

St. Alphonsus taught that mediate material cooperation could be justified if there is a "serious reason" to cooperate and if scandal could be avoided. Scandal is defined by St. Thomas as "any word or deed not fully upright which is the occasion of sin to another."[14] Father Ludvico Bender says:

> [A]ctive scandal is unbecoming conduct in act, word, or omission which is the occasion of spiritual harm to another. Sometimes actions, not evil in themselves, have nevertheless the appearance of evil and as such may lead another to sin.[15]

This latter situation is the real possibility when partnerships are mediate material cooperation. The public perception of the Catholic hospital's cooperation may be such that it appears that the Catholic partner is compromising or contradicting the professed teachings of the Church.

This type of scandal occurs in the board room as well as in the community. It is very difficult to explain the principles of cooperation in a way that holds the attention of one's listeners. The fundamental touchstone of these principles is the objective moral

---

[14] See St. Thomas Aquinas, *Summa Theologiae*, II-II, 43, 1.

[15] Ludovico Bender, O.P., "Scandal" in *Dictionary of Moral Theology*, ed. Pietro Palazzini (Westminster, Md.: The Newman Press, 1962), 1096. See Smith, "Principles of Cooperation," 224.

order which one is not free to violate. But living in a fallen world, the morally upright person will encounter the intentional evil of others, and unless one withdraws from all involvement in the world (sectarianism), one must cooperate in ways that do not involve evil intentions or intrinsically evil acts. The careful distinctions that have a certain clarity on the blackboard of the theology department lose their focus in the minds of practical Anglo-Saxons. We are often accused—explicitly or implicitly—of winking and nodding, of rationalizing, or in religious language, of Phariseeism. This can only be avoided by constant, living contact between the articulation of the principles of cooperation and the first principle of morality, "do good and avoid evil."

The scandal that must be avoided then, can be defined as:

> *The proposal or execution of a course of action that either is or has the potential of being perceived as constituting a contradiction or compromise of the Church's teaching with the effect that the Catholic partner is or appears to be doing evil, giving bad example, making evil appear to be good or upright, and/or suggesting that others can embark upon this evil with impunity.*

Immediate Material Cooperation

Immediate material cooperation has been a focus of some attention in the literature of the last year. And this topic is perhaps the most important thing I can address in this talk. In the dossier of items entitled *Catholic Health Ministry in Transition*, it is repeatedly asserted that immediate material cooperation is permissible for a proportionate reason. I cannot state emphatically enough that this is a gratuitous assertion which contradicts the theological teaching regarding the principles of cooperation from the time of St. Alphonsus. The impermissibility of immediate material cooperation in the tradition is noted by Father Charles Curran in his article on the history of the principles.[16] To assert now that such cooperation is possible "for a proportionate reason" is novel and unproven.

It is said that the "proportionate reason" justifying immediate material cooperation is duress (which will be examined next). But this too is untraditional since duress mitigates the subjective guilt of the cooperator, rendering the cooperator something of a hostage by compromising freedom of action. By

---

[16] Charles Curran, "Cooperation in a Pluralistic Society," *Ongoing Revision in Moral Theology* (Notre Dame, Ind.: Fides/Claretian, 1975), 210-228.

contrast, immediate material cooperation was understood as the free action of the cooperator, which, while not intrinsically evil, has intimate involvement in the evil of the principal agent. Recall the example condemned by the Inquisition in 1679. Here the Church taught that the servant's action of carrying a ladder for his master to climb into a woman's room was to be considered morally wrong. Note: the Church had no need to condemn the action of the master because everyone recognized its intrinsic evil. The action of the servant was morally indifferent—prescinding from the circumstances. However, the morally indifferent act was corrupted by its intimate association with the crime of the principal agent. What was condemned in 1679 was immediate material cooperation.

It was the verdict of the Magisterium that intimate involvement with the immoral acts of others can corrupt even morally indifferent acts of cooperation. One cannot directly contribute even in a material way to the evil acts of others. The clerk in the liquor store is engaged in proximate material cooperation with a particular client's alcoholism, but the bartender is engaged in immediate material cooperation. It is therefore important to focus on the distinction between immediate and mediate material cooperation, not on that between formal and immediate material cooperation. Again, duress implies loss of control and therefore a crippling of the voluntary.

> *Immediate material cooperation, then, is the performance of a morally good or indifferent action which is inherently and intimately bound to the performance of an evil action on the part of the principal agent, in such a way that the evil action of the principal agent stands as a defining or morally significant circumstance of the cooperator's action which corrupts its moral species such that it is rendered impermissible.*

Duress

Duress is a vague, and therefore, broadly understood concept. *Webster's Third New International Dictionary* defines duress as:

> **1:** restraint or check by force...**2:** stringent compulsion by threat of danger, hardship, or retribution...**3:** compulsion or constraint by which a person is illegally forced to do or forbear some act by actual imprisonment or physical

violence to the person or by threat of such violence, the violence or threat being such as to inspire a person of ordinary firmness with fear of serious injury to the person..., reputation, or fortune.

The element of duress was addressed in the *Commentary on the Reply of the Sacred Congregation for the Doctrine of the Faith on Sterilization in Catholic Hospitals.* There one reads:

Material cooperation will be justified only in situations where the hospital because of some kind of duress or pressure cannot reasonably exercise the autonomy it has....
Direct sterilization is a grave evil. The allowance of material cooperation in extraordinary cases is based on the danger of an even more serious evil, e.g., the closing of the hospital could be under certain circumstance a more serious evil.

Also, it states:

In making judgments about the morality of cooperation each case must be decided on its own merits. Since hospital situations, and even individual cases, differ so much, it would not be prudent to apply automatically a decision made in one hospital, or even in one case, to another.

Here, one discerns the nature of the duress which the NCCB (and the Congregation for the Doctrine of the Faith) has in mind. Authors who write about duress stress the fact that duress should not "be exaggerated to justify any cooperation in wrongdoing;"[17] therefore, an analysis and expounding of the relevant Church documents on this point would seem to be helpful. In light of the dictionary's definition of duress and the ecclesiastical documents' description of elements of licit responses to duress, it seems that the following elements are considered essential.

First, duress arises from a situation of coercion or compulsion against a certain party. Duress implies threat and force to such a degree that the victim of this duress has a reasonable loss of will in light of the situation. This element of fear or threat removes this from the realm of the purely voluntary *in an ethically significant sense,* and therefore, from the realm of *the principles of cooperation as they were conceived in the tradition.* Here one crosses the threshold of

[17] James F. Keenan, S.J. and Thomas R. Kopfensteiner, "The Principle of Cooperation," *Health Progress,* vol. 76, no. 3 (April 1995), 25.

impediments of human (moral) acts, whereas the principles of cooperation as they are delineated in the textbooks remain in the arena of the voluntary. Duress implies significant characteristics of the hostage who may perform acts identical to those of an accomplice, but whose involvement in the act of the principal agent is purely instrumental, not voluntary. That is why this is *not* immediate material cooperation in the way the tradition has understood it.

Second, the NCCB understands such duress to be rare, that is, "episodic," to the extent that the reasons allowing for the involvement of Catholic providers in the business of sterilization cannot be articulated in the form of a policy that could be shared among hospitals nor even between one case and another in the same facility. "Since hospital situations, and even individual cases, differ so much, it would not be prudent to apply automatically a decision made in one hospital, or even in one case, to another." This episodic character of which the documents speak is important to ponder and to consider in light of what hospital administrators and sponsors are describing as "systemic duress," understood generally as market pressure or physician demands. There seems to be some disparity between the documents' understanding of duress as a relatively rare occurrence of horrific proportions and some administrators' belief that duress is a pressure of ever increasing force which is inherent in the very matrix of health care and which demands a uniformity of provision of services and that the non-compliance therewith entails gradual strangulation and eventual closure by withdrawal of professionals and their referrals. As evidence of this, administrators of Catholic hospitals point to dwindling OB/GYN admissions and foresee a decline in pediatrics as this specialty will be treating children through the age of eighteen, with all the challenges of adolescence.

From a different direction, viz., from the philosophical community, there may be some relief from this disparity of understanding. According to the dons, duress has both episodic and systemic characteristics. Indeed, it is compulsion to perform certain actions which one would otherwise be unwilling to perform, but is coerced to do through threat of injury, death, or other damage *which has been sanctioned and mandated by legal authority of the state.* Here, for example, one finds that certain states require all HMOs operative within their jurisdiction to provide contraceptive services by force of law. Catholic sponsors can embark upon engagement in ownership or partnership with HMOs only by "providing for the non-provision" of contraceptive services on our part through the creation of third party underwriters and the like that do what we would not involve ourselves in. (This is what Professor Grisez calls formal cooperation and what many consider Phariseeism on our part.)

Until there is a meeting of the minds on the nature of duress regarding its systemic expression, an operative definition may be formulated as follows:

> *Duress is an exceptional (episodic) compulsion to perform certain non-death-dealing procedures which are not permitted by the* Ethical and Religious Directives, *so strong as to render the Catholic provider constrained to comply or suffer grave, catastrophic loss to the mission. Duress does not strictly fall under the principles of cooperation, but rather under the non-voluntary principles of compliance under force.*

While Catholic hospitals must insist on their sovereign rights of ownership and conscience, it is theoretically possible to imagine scenarios of legalized (ergo systemic) formalities which produce structures of permanent or persistent duress habitually inhibiting the freedom of hospital administration in certain areas. However, such systemic duress would impel the Catholic sponsor to consider both negotiated dispensation from the requirements of law and/or the possibility of modification of the apostolate.

An example of systemic duress is the legal impediment of the Church to engage in religious instruction in some countries. The duress is systemic inasmuch as the law impedes the Church from engaging in the activity by threat of legal sanction and perhaps suppression ("the more serious evil" mentioned in the NCCB's reply). However, this example is not analogous because the non-provision of religious instruction results from a legal impediment to engaging in a certain action, whereas in the hospital setting, what is being addressed is that duress which would force one to engage in the *performance* of an act considered immoral. There is a great difference between being prohibited from doing a good thing, and being forced to do something evil. Also, the moral reflex responds differently to the two scenarios: with regret in both, but with a hope in patient endurance when impeded from being free to teach the faith, and with a sense of anger resulting from a certain defilement at having been forced into being an instrument of evil in the case of engaging in an act we believe to be evil.

Two Problematical Applications

In conclusion, I would like to mention two items of concern to sponsors, administrators, and bishops. The first regards the shape and direction of health care delivery evolution through the creation of integrated delivery networks (IDN). One of the most vexing questions is what is the evolution going to lead us to in five, ten, fifteen years. Today, individual hospitals are joining together to form management corporations which are being given broad and deep powers of control over the various hospitals in the network to "rationalize" care. In general, the individual hospitals remain owned by the respective sponsors (Catholic or non-Catholic), each retains its own board of directors, and each sponsor remains the sole member of the hospital's corporation. It is foreseen that these management corporations are themselves becoming the center of health care delivery and tend to assume ever increasing authority over the hospitals. It is argued that for efficiency, the management corporation should become a holding company, which itself becomes the sole corporate member of the hospitals. (The members of the holding company are the collective sponsors of the hospitals.) Note that in this schema, the Catholic sponsor is no longer the sole member of the apostolate's corporation. The question is: if actual control of the hospital in the areas we regard as the domain of reserved powers can be given to the religious sponsors through contractual arrangement with the holding company, is this enough to constitute Catholic identity? In other words, is practical *control* enough to constitute *sponsorship* (not defined in the *Code of Canon Law*), in the face of the cessation of *ownership*? It seems to me that if the assets of the hospital are sold to a (non-Catholic) holding company, there is certainly alienation of property. But another question arises: if the religious congregation can retain *control* of the elements of reserved powers, can this hospital still be considered to be Catholic? What constitutes Catholic sponsorship: ownership, control, or both?

The second item of concern relates to the purchase of physicians' practices. The writing of prescriptions for oral contraceptives is increasingly problematical. In my encounters with physicians and religious sponsors throughout the country, it has been my experience that there is emerging consensus that professionals' practice cannot be "owned" in the usual sense of the word. They are not technicians nor mere instruments of a corporation. Their professional persona is larger than their "employment contract." If they prescribe oral contraceptives, it should not be done as an agent of their employer, but as a private professional. This means that it must be written on their own (not St. Swithun's) prescription pad, which means they are solely liable for their action and its outcome.

Conclusion

Can the soul of Catholic health care be saved? Certainly, its body is changing rapidly. As Charles Osgood says, "as I get older, I realize my body is playing by different rules." This is true of health care. But I hope that the changes in the body signal a development in maturity rather than being symptomatic of terminal illness. Let us hope that these changes are the dawn of mid-life rather than the departure of the soul at death.

CHAPTER 9

From Cairo to Beijing: Behind the Headlines

HELEN ALVARÉ, J.D.

The "International Conference on Population and Development" and the "Fourth World Conference on Women," sponsored by the United Nations in Cairo and Beijing, respectively, received widespread attention from the media. Reporters watched every move made by the competing parties almost like a sports event. During the Cairo conference in particular, the morning talk shows never failed to contain debates by advocates on each side of the issues. For the most part, the media covering Cairo concentrated on abortion, and to a lesser extent, disputes over contraception and population theories. During the Beijing conference, the media addressed these topics, but also "gay rights" (with special attention to the seminar on "lesbian flirting techniques" presented by non-governmental organizations), private property rights for Muslim women, genital mutilation, and access to private credit for women. Not surprisingly, subjects that the media could group under the label of "sex" garnered disproportionate attention at Beijing as well.

In some ways, the media accurately characterized the nub of each of the controversies in Cairo. In one important way, however, they missed the boat. For what became even clearer in Beijing than even in Cairo was this: the competing visions about particular issues—birth control, abortion, or parental rights and responsibilities regarding their minor daughters—were but the most visible evidence of competing visions about the broader matter of the appropriate and desirable role(s) for women in the modern world. And one understands best the intensity with which disputes over discrete matters were conducted, only if one also understands the world views from which they arise.

In this essay, I will consider those competing world views and comment upon the exchanges between the United States and the Holy See over these matters and upon the effort by a very few to oust the Holy See from member status in future UN international conferences.

Vision I:
Women as Individualistic Actors
in a Market Economy

In order to get a feeling for the ideas and the ideologies that inform the world view against which the Holy See competed in Cairo and Beijing, it is useful to turn to the documents produced by the Women's Economic and Development Organization (WEDO), a non-govenmental organization that has official status, but disproportionate influence at the UN, in part because of the close relationship its director, Bella Abzug, has with many at the UN, including several members of the delegation from the United States. WEDO published many preparatory documents in advance of both Beijing and Cairo. These documents reveal that their views are similar to the views of the major organized feminist and population control groups with whom they deal and to the views of some of the more noteworthy members of the United States delegation with whom they are influential—like Geraldine Ferraro and Marjorie Margolies Mezvinsky. In quick strokes, one could characterize them this way.

First, they are permeated with a strong sense of the past oppression of women.

Second, they believe that major agents of past oppression include not only men generally, but especially religion, marriage, and motherhood.

Third, they believe that overcoming past oppression equals achieving virtual sameness with men. These groups are uncomfortable with almost any discussion of differences between men and women. They will not outright deny that there are differences, but neither will they ever make these differences a focus for discussion of the roles that women might play in modern society. Their common mode of operation, therefore, is to seek absolute equality with men—understanding "equality" to mean achieving the same outcomes as men.

Fourth, according to those who take this view of equality, the "outcome" that describes men's roles in the world most accurately is that they are free to achieve career and economic success in the public square. Men do not have primary nurturing responsibility for their children. They are not primarily defined by whether they are married with children, but by their level of success in the public square. All institutions—academic, financial, political, legal, and the like—are set up to accommodate men in their path to success. Women, on the other hand, are, at present, primarily defined by their relationship to others: their husbands, their children, their parents. When women try to succeed in the public square, they are actively disadvantaged by the major academic, financial, political, legal and other institutions. Religion too holds them down. It encourages them to suppress their potential for success so that they can serve their husbands, children, and families generally.

According to WEDO, women must be freed from these disadvantages in order to have success in the same way that men have it. They must not be bound by stifling notions of how important mothering is or how important marriage and the family are. They must be freed up from these. And freed up from the bonds imposed by religion and religious institutions. The Cairo and Beijing documents must, therefore, be crafted so as to minimize the importance—in the lives of women, men, or their families—of marriage, motherhood, family, or religion. At the very least, these ought to be mentioned rarely. At best, they ought to be called into question as, for example, sources of domestic violence, degradation of women's health, and the like.

Fifth, the capacity of women to bear children—which most intrudes on the world's ability to see women and men as the same—must therefore be placed into women's absolute control so that they can do what it takes to lessen the effects that children have on women's lives and that they do not normally have on men's lives.

Sixth, the primary way they hope to do this is to "equalize" the outcomes of sexual intercourse for men and women. Men can have sexual intercourse and not find themselves pregnant. Women can get pregnant. This group of feminists and population control advocates seeks to "solve" this by contraception. Then, no matter what sex you are, you do not have to be pregnant after intercourse. Public education and huge amounts of public monies must be directed to contraception. Even if other projects must be shortchanged—projects like education and holistic care, which could bring long-term benefits to women—immediate access to contraception remains critical.

But, of course, contraception fails. In the United States, 50% of the patients going into Planned Parenthoood clinics for abortions say that they were using contraception at the time they got pregnant. This represents a considerable number of failures in the United States, where there is widespread education about contraceptive techniques. Can one even imagine what the failure rates for contraception must be in poorer countries around the world? Therefore, these feminist and population control advocates support abortion. For in the practical sense, morality aside, abortion is the key to absolute control over one's childbearing. And absolute control, an absolute ability not to be pregnant, like men are never pregnant, is what they want, and nothing less.

Countries supporting this vision included Canada, the European Union, some African countries like Namibia and Zimbabwe, and—despite their rhetoric in advance—the United States. The European Union was particularly bold and unabashed in its advocacy of rights for homosexuals and unbridled sexual rights generally.

Vision II:
The Teaching of the Holy See

The Holy See's vision of women begins first with its support for the inherent dignity of women and their fundamental equality with men. Because God created both man and woman, because both are in the image and likeness of God, both are inherently good.

Second, the Holy See acknowledged past failures, by the Church and by the larger society, to give due importance to women's equality.

Third, as a standard for achieving progress for women, the Holy See did not propose a model of "equality as sameness." Rather, the Holy See proposed a model of complementarity. This notion of complementarity is not a rigid model. In many ways, it acts like an invitation for the world to reflect upon the different modes of behavior and roles that women and men have assumed in cultures around the world, over many thousands of years. It does not precisely assign women particular roles, although it holds that, given women's unique relationship with new life, they hold special rights and responsibilities in connection with the bearing and raising of children. At the same time, however, the Holy See asserted strongly the rightful place of women in the public square. It praised those women who have valiantly fought for it, and even expressed sorrow that some have called them "unfeminine." The Holy See suggests that accommodations will have to be made in the larger society in order that women can exercise their rights and fulfill their responsibilities both to family and to the public square. The Holy See was not afraid to acknowledge that sometimes, for truly fair treatment, differences must be noted, and accommodations made.

On a practical note, the Holy See spoke for the millions of women who do marry, who do want husbands, who both want and have children, and who do find happiness and even freedom in the practice of their faith. The Holy See suggested that instead of throwing these babies out with the bathwater, certain feminists ought to try their hands at improving them.

Fourth, and almost needless to say, the Holy See did not jump on the birth control bandwagon. The contraceptive mentality, it held, could not truly free women, but could only act as another constraint on them. This is true on a practical level not only because of the difficult and sometimes dangerous side effects of artificial birth control, but because of the temptation—which governments never seem able to avoid—to begin imposing contraception and a contraceptive mentality upon women from without.

Fifth, understanding that stripping women of their roles as mothers, wives, and members of religious faiths is not the answer, the Holy See suggested rather that what was really needed was resources for women to improve their access to and opportunities in the public square. The Holy See, therefore, called for a generous infusion of monies and time into programs for women in education, health care, access to credit, and the like. It recognized, too, the desperate need for public and private policies to support women's and men's abilities to serve both their families and their work in the public square.

In the end, for both women and men, the Holy See rejected the individualistic model in favor of a model recognizing and valuing relationships within families, communities, and religious faiths. It rejected attempts to send women into the public square armed only with contraception and abortion—stripped of all support from family, church, and state.

The United States and the Holy See

There was much acrimony between the Clinton Administration, its representatives to Cairo, and the Holy See in 1994 before, during, and after the International Conference on Population and Development. The contentious issue that received the most attention was the White House's documented attempt, via its State Department, to urge every country participating in the Cairo conference to have the final Cairo document include a fundamental right to abortion. This received widespread publicity, even appearing on the front pages of papers like the *Washington Post* and the *New York Times*. In my public appearances on television at that time to speak in favor of the Holy See, the tension and anger I felt from opponents and from the interviewers was far greater than I remember experiencing when abortion was at issue in the strictly domestic context. At one point, the head of the United States delegation, Undersecretary of State Tim Wirth, flatly refused to appear on any morning talk shows with me.

During this same year, John Paul II was named Man of the Year by *Time*, his book, *Crossing the Threshold of Hope*, was hitting the best-seller lists, and *Veritatis splendor* was drawing attention in both secular and sectarian arenas. In consequence, the White House grew less and less comfortable being in a public hissing contest with Joaquin Navarro-Valls and the Holy See generally.

In light of this, serious efforts were made by the White House to "tone down" public exchanges with the Holy See prior to the Beijing conference. Public statements were issued by the White House indicating that they had no intention of seeking to get the Beijing document to declare a right to abortion. They made general promises not to "go beyond" Cairo language in areas like contraception. A few days prior to the conference, Hillary Clinton's staff called and asked if we could meet to discuss the upcoming conference. We met, and our time together consisted mostly in their assurances that the delegations from the United States and the Holy See would have a lot in common at Beijing. At the preparatory meetings in advance of the Beijing conference in New York, Gail Quinn noted that the United States assisted the Holy See here and there in small matters that arose.

In Beijing itself, one could say that the tone of the interactions between the United States and the Holy See was mild. This was not so much an indication that the United States had changed its negotiating interests, but that other delegations carried the water on the more controversial matters that arose. It was also because the United States delegation sought indirect methods to achieve things opposed by the Holy See. Even so, with respect to abortion and birth control, the United States delegation eventually did oppose the Holy See.

Movement to Oust the Holy See

In Beijing there was a petition to oust the Holy See from the United Nations. This petition was signed by few people, but the few included members of official delegations from other countries. This was an undiplomatic way in which to behave at such a conference. (Discussions such as these would ordinarily be conducted at high levels, not in the form of a petition). This movement was spearheaded, not unexpectedly, by the group calling themselves "Catholics for a Free Choice."

This move was not about the Holy See's unique composition as a nation-state. It was about exorcising a particular viewpoint from the discussion of highly controversial issues like world population, the roles of women in the modern world, abortion, contraception, and human sexuality generally. Outside of Beijing, the most attention this effort received was in a *New York Times* op-ed piece by Frances Kissling, head of the previously mentioned Catholics for a Free Choice.

This failed attempt to remove the Holy See from the United Nations probably does not amount to a serious threat to the Holy See's place in the United Nations at the present time. Still, the significance of this sort of movement is exaggerated by those who thrive on creating as much trouble as possible for the Catholic

Church generally and the Holy See in particular. Given the support offered by the Holy See in the course of the founding of the United Nations, the longevity of its involvement, and the relationships forged over years of diplomatic relationships, the Holy See is not likely to be ousted (in the near future).

CHAPTER 10

From Cairo to Beijing: The Catholic Response

THE MOST REVEREND JAMES T. McHUGH

During the past quarter century there has been increasing interest in and concern about population growth, particularly in the developing nations of the world. Population growth has moved from the realm of careful demographic research to the area of popular and political debate. This has been aided by the high visibility given population issues by the United Nations sponsored international conferences in 1974, 1984, and 1994. Unfortunately the higher visibility has not increased public understanding and the misleading forecasts of groups and organizations committed to population control have had the desired effect of confusing the issues and creating an atmosphere of fear. During the 1960s the argument was that the increase in population would result in a decline in food, water, economic resources and it would do irreparable damage to the environment. This argument was most forcefully presented by Paul Ehrlich and Garrett Hardin, among others.[1] More recently this approach has been countered by Julian

---

[1] See for instance: P. Ehrlich, *The Population Bomb* (New York: Ballantine Books, 1968); G. Hardin, "The Tragedy of the Commons," *Science*, Dec. 13, 1968, and *Exploring*

Simon, Paul Bauer and others who argue that a reasonable increase in population means more producers and consumers, and modern technology enables us to overcome a depletion of natural resources by the discovery of other abundant resources or by substituting synthetic products for natural ones.[2]

Nathan Keyfitz has provided an insightful explanation for the wide divergence of opinion on population. Early in the debates, the apocalyptic approach regarding population growth came from biologists who used a biological model. These dealt with closed systems and foresaw great danger in any population growth. On the other hand there were the economists, who saw population growth or decline as one aspect of the overall economic picture, which could be addressed in different ways, especially by socio-economic development.[3]

Presently the debate has shifted to a concern about the "carrying capacity" of the earth, a concept that is not easily definable nor demographically provable. A companion idea that has gained more political support, especially in United Nations debates, is "sustainable development." Yet, there are still serious disagreements about the precise definition of these terms and their implications. In a recent article, Joel Cohen has raised a series of questions pertinent to defining "carrying capacity" but he ends with the conclusion that "the question, 'How many people can the earth support?' has no single numerical answer, now or ever."[4]

In the face of the apocalyptic predictions of the extent and impact of global population growth—some project a population of 694 billion people in 2150 if populations continue to grow at 1990 rates—it is important to look at the more careful and limited projections of the United Nations, which are generally used as benchmarks by population scientists.

In 1992 the United Nations medium range estimate of world population was 5.5 billion people. By 2025 that figure is expected to increase to 8.5 billion people. World population is expected to stabilize at 10.1 billion in 2080. At the same time, present world

New Ethics for Survival (Baltimore, Md.: Penguin Books, 1973); and additional works by both authors.

[2] J. Simon, *The Ultimate Resource* (Princeton, N.J.: Princeton Univ. Press, 1981), *Population and Development in Poor Countries* (Princeton, 1992), and additional works; P. Bauer, *Equality, The Third World and Economic Delusion* (Cambridge, Mass.: Harvard Univ. Press, 1981) and *The Development Frontier* (Harvard, 1991).

[3] N. Keyfitz, "Demographic Discord," *The Sciences*, September/October 1994.

[4] J. Cohen, "How Many People Can the Earth Support?" *The Sciences*, November/December 1995.

growth rates show a general decline, and UN population studies indicate that we will experience a new stage of population decrease in the mid-1990s. These estimates, of course, vary from continent to continent, and from nation to nation. In some countries, growth rates are still quite high; in others, they are below population stabilization, that is, 2.1 children per family. Population assessments are complex, and while actual numbers of people will increase, population rates will decrease. In summary, long-range projections are always tenuous and a simple recitation of numerical calculations is often misleading.

To understand the implication of these figures, one must understand that the pace of the actual increase in people will begin to slow considerably after 2010, because the rate of the world's population growth has already been in decline. The rate of growth was at a peak of 2.1 percent in the years 1965–1970, declining to 1.67 percent in the years 1980–1985, and is expected to fall to 1 percent by the year 2025, continuing the downward trend until the end of the twenty-first century.[5]

The major factors affecting world population are fertility, mortality, and migration. Thus, by way of summary, we can draw the following profile of the world's population:

1. The major cause of the decline of population growth has been the decline in birth rates. Rates in the developed nations have fallen most sharply, with the majority of the developed nations presently below the replacement level of 2.1 children per woman of childbearing age. Rates in the developing nations have also begun to decline. Decline has been rapid in North Africa, Latin America and most of Asia, while rates of fertility are high in sub-Saharan Africa and Western Asia. China had a 1985–1990 rate of 2.1.

2. Mortality rates are also decreasing. Mortality is best measured in terms of life expectancy. Life expectancy at birth in the years 1985–1990 was projected to be 61.1 years for the world, 74.0 for developed nations, and 59.0 for the developing nations. Among the latter, infant mortality is highest in Africa (101 infant deaths per 1,000 live births) and lowest in Latin America (56 per 1,000 live births). In all cases, there has been a notable decline in mortality since 1975.

[5] See *World Population Prospect: The 1992 Revision* (New York: United Nations, 1993).

3. The changes in births and deaths affect the population structure of countries. In the developing nations, there are higher proportions of children and youths. In 1985, there were 570 million children under 5 years of age in the world, 85 percent in the developing nations. At the other end of the life span, in 1985, 8.8 percent of the world's population were persons 60 years of age or older. The percentage was 15.8 in the developed nations and 6.6 in the developing nations. Note however that the elderly population has been growing much faster, and the aging of the population is an increasingly important concern in all regions and nations because it affects social security for the elderly and a decreasing work force.

4. While the actual numbers of international migrants are not generally large, the impact of migration is significant. In countries that have promoted permanent resettlement (Argentina, Australia, Canada, Israel, and the United States) and those of Western Europe that have imported laborers, the numbers are higher. Other nations had significant numbers due to temporary labor needs, dislocation due to war or partition, or permissive immigration policies. In many cases, international migration is a consequence of a country's need for younger and sometimes unskilled workers and the corresponding need of people to find employment in another country. This pattern is also evident in regard to internal migration, where increasing numbers of young people are relocating from agricultural areas to major cities.

Although rates of population increase have declined, not all population problems have been solved. Indeed, the problems go far beyond the statistical reports and projections. The rates of growth and decline must be analyzed in reference to other variables—food, employment, housing, health care, education, natural resources and environment, and the world economic outlook.[6] These factors have a more direct bearing on people's lives—and lifestyles—and sharpen the moral and ethical sensitivity regarding human dignity, social justice, and the common good. Thus, while the decline in population growth has defused the population bomb, the development process has not moved

[6] See J. McHugh, "Facts, Morality and Population Issues," *The Priest*, August 1994.

forward at an equal pace in all parts of the world, and great global inequities still exist. This further emphasizes the need for population policies that are based on religious and human values and are informed by moral and ethical principles.

The Teaching of the Church on Population

In the context of the gloom-doom forecasts of the 1960s and 1970s, it was not infrequently argued that all measures to limit population growth should be taken, including some that were directly or implicitly coercive. Furthermore, the Catholic Church was often described as a major causal agent of world population growth because of its moral teaching opposing artificial contraception, sterilization, and abortion.

At the same time, the Catholic Church was developing a moral-ethical position on population policy. Note that population control and birth control are not the same thing. Population control is what governments and international agencies do, while birth control is what couples do. In any case, while the roots of the Church's position on population policy can be found in its social teaching of the past one hundred years, Paul VI and John Paul II have refined and specifically applied the Church's teaching on the dignity of the human person, social justice, and responsible parenthood to contemporary population issues. We find this development in conciliar and synodal documents, in papal addresses, and in the interventions of delegations of the Holy See to international meetings on population and socio-economic concerns.[7]

The core concerns of the Holy See were strongly articulated in the preparations for and the actual conduct of the 1994 "International Conference on Population and Development" held in Cairo, Egypt. Pope John Paul II met on March 18, 1994, with Dr. Nafis Sadik and stated the concerns of the Church, with particular reference to the preparatory agenda document for the Cairo meeting. The pope followed the preparatory meetings

[7] See Paul VI to Antonio Carillo-Flores and Rafael Salas, March 28, 1974; Document of Committee for the Family, 1974; Intervention of Bishop Edouard Gagnon, Head of Holy See Delegation to World Population Conference, Bucharest, 1974; John Paul II to Rafael Salas, June 7, 1984; Address of Archbishop Jan Schotte, Chairman of Vatican Delegation to the United Nations Population Conference, Mexico City, 1984; John Paul II to Nafis Sadik, March 18, 1994; Archbishop R. Martino, Intervention of Holy See Delegation at Cairo Conference, Sept. 1994; also Pontifical Council for the Family, "Population Trends: Ethical and Pastoral Dimensions," in *Origins*, August 4, 1994.

carefully and foresaw the emerging effort to use Cairo to establish an internationally recognized right to abortion. This prompted a letter to the leader of each country in the world, contacts by the Vatican diplomatic corps, personal contacts with some world leaders, including President William Clinton, and a series of audience talks in the weeks leading to the Cairo conference. The following core principles were stated clearly and were the primary issues put forth in the address of Archbishop Renato Martino, head of the Vatican's delegation at Cairo.

1. Population policy should be a part of a more comprehensive commitment to policies and programs of human development and social justice that enable all persons to live a fully human life, one endowed with freedom and dignity. At the center of all concern about social development is the human person, created in the image of God and redeemed by Jesus Christ. Human dignity and human rights derive from the unique status and identity of the human person. But every person lives in society, perhaps many societies, which must protect and sustain the rights of each person but which also requires solidarity among all persons to protect and enhance the common good. Further, this human solidarity and commitment to the common good lead to appropriate stewardship of all creation, including the environment, and an appropriate sharing of created goods.

2. Population growth and decline are issues of social concern and affect the development process. Governments have rights and duties in attempting to ameliorate population problems and in addressing population variables. It is not simply a matter of births and deaths, but includes among other things, concern for children and the aging, the stability of the family, migration, economic processes, and concern about health issues and delivery of health services.

3. The family is the basic social unit and the stability and well-being of the family is a basic moral principle in dealing with social problems and development issues. Society has a responsibility to protect and sustain the family by appropriate laws and social policies. The family should be protected from pressures that prevent it from

pursuing its legitimate goals, especially in regard to the size of the family and the spacing of births, and it should be given assistance by society in regard to education, stable social and economic conditions, and the welfare of all its members. Society should create an environment of security for the family and shape social and economic policies to assist families with special needs.

4. Decisions regarding the size of the family and the frequency of births should be made by the parents, without pressure from the government. Such decisions are based on a correctly formed conscience that respects the Church's authentic interpretation of the divine law in regard to family planning methods. The principle of responsible parenthood asserts that, in reaching their decisions, couples should take into account their responsibilities to God, themselves, the children they already have, and the community or society to which they belong.

5. Women enjoy fundamental human rights as persons who are equal to men and who share partnership with men in regard to the common good, and especially in the family. Society is enriched when women enjoy freedom, dignity, and equality. Education, health care, economic and professional opportunities, and societal recognition of their family roles should be assured for all women.

6. A fundamental dimension of human personhood is the personal relationship with God and society should recognize the importance of religious faith and moral principles and ensure religious freedom for all persons.

The Cairo Conference

The "International Conference on Population and Development" took place in Cairo, September 5-13, 1994. The United Nations sponsored previous international conferences in Bucharest (1974) and Mexico City (1984). The Holy See sent a delegation to each of these conferences, and as noted above, had developed a consistent set of core principles that guided the activity of the delegation. The Holy See did not join the consensus that adopted the final document in either Bucharest or Mexico City, but a new tactic was used in Cairo whereby the Holy See joined the consensus but only in a partial manner. Archbishop Martino explained this decision by noting some positive accomplishments of the conference, such as increased attention to the linkage of population and development, support for the family as traditionally understood, recognition of the rights and roles of women, consideration of migration issues, exclusion of any type of coercion in population and family planning programs, and respect for religious and cultural beliefs. While these were positive aspects of the final document, they were not always clear nor unburdened by alternate understandings unacceptable to the Holy See.[8]

At the same time, the final document fell far short on some specific issues that were related to the Holy See's core principles, and though there were vast improvements as a result of the deliberations and open debate, many of the final formulations remained fundamentally unacceptable.

The "Programme of Action" was adopted at the final session of the Cairo Conference on September 13, 1994. In addition to the Holy See, twenty other nations expressed reservations or rejection of certain parts of the document, a large measure of dissent for a UN conference. Most of the objections came in regard to chapters or paragraphs on the family or on abortion. Following is an analysis of the document with an explanation of the reservations or rejections of the pertinent sections by the Holy See.

Population and Development

The conference was entitled the "International Conference on Population and Development," but development received very little attention. The various chapters of the "Programme of Action" (hereafter *PA*) fail to focus on demographic variables and their impact on and relationship to development strategies and programs. So for instance, the preamble states as the "important population and development objectives" of the *PA*:

–sustained economic growth in the context of sustainable development

–education, especially for girls; gender equity and equality; infant, child, and maternal mortality reduction

–the provision of universal access to reproductive health services, including family planning and sexual health

[8] See *Population and Development*, Vol. 1 (New York: United Nations, 1995). Archbishop Martino's explanation of the Vatican position is included in an appendix to the "Programme of Action" as adopted in Cairo.

Most of the *PA* deals with the third of these objectives, and one could say that this is the controlling factor for the *PA*.

"Universal access to family planning" was seen as the primary approach to development. It was assumed that there was a vast unmet need for family planning services, which if met, would lower birth rates and thereby improve socio-economic conditions. This is a very simplistic and unproven assumption.[9]

The demographic estimates and projections were not carefully analyzed nor related to the demographic variables. Consequently, the raw figures tend to create the impression that development efforts are doomed to frustration unless there is a drastic decline in fertility, especially in developing nations. The *PA* assumes that the attainment of population stabilization is an internationally agreed upon goal and that it can only be achieved during the twenty-first century if "all the policies and recommendations in the present Plan of Action" are implemented as quickly as possible. While there is widespread recognition that global population cannot increase without any restraint forever, there is also considerable debate about the necessity of absolute population stabilization, that is, zero growth, or whether some moderate growth can be sustained. There is also a more general agreement that growth and decline have different implications in different areas of the world.

Access to the family planning methods of one's choice and methods for the regulation of fertility of one's choice that are not against the law are continually promoted throughout the *PA*. The emphasis on access is especially objectionable because it is almost always stated as a duty or responsibility of governments or other organizations to provide such access. Furthermore, the emphasis on access includes the unmarried, teenagers, and migrants, without any evaluation of the impact on the family. It is based on an individualistic attitude toward sexual freedom and behavior.

Rights Language

The *PA* asserts rights that are not based on internationally recognized human rights. "Rights language" prevails throughout the final document, although there were concerted efforts during the preparatory meetings about Cairo to eliminate such language. The original effort was to assert sexual rights and reproductive rights that would include abortion as a universally accepted

[9] See "Battle of the Bulge," *The Economist*, September 3, 1994.

human right. The Holy See, most of the Arab states and other nations opposed the extensive and unnuanced use of rights language, and much of it was eliminated from the final *PA*. However, it was often replaced by vague formulations, and in light of the original intent, many nations expressed their opposition to the terms "sexual rights" and "reproductive rights."

The Family

Chapter 5 of the final *PA* was improved over the Prep Comm documents. But it still contains a measure of vagueness and in some cases, family prerogatives are assigned to others outside the family by other chapters of the *PA*. Many of the attitudes are not consistent with Catholic teaching on the family. This was one of the strong points made by John Paul II in his addresses and audience talks in June, July, and August of 1994.

The final version of the *PA* returns to the classic UN formulation that "the family is the basic unit of society." This formulation is important because it establishes the well-being and stability of the family, traditionally understood, as a societal concern and responsibility, and it obligates governments to protect, sustain, and support the family. This philosophy is present in many UN documents and is reflected in the family policy of many nations. It received non-support, if not opposition from American delegates because the United States does not have a family policy and because American social policy is based on an untempered emphasis on individualism.

So, for instance, the opening words of chapter 5, "While various forms of the family exist...." is a change from the earlier language "While various concepts...." The change was negotiated by the Islamic nations and the European Union. The word forms is used throughout the text. Caution should be exercised since "forms" is never clearly defined. If it is intended to mean an institutionalized form, that is, a family form rooted in fact or everyday experience with or without legal sanction, it may include things like polygamous marriage, homosexual unions, cohabitation, and serial marriage. In a more limited definition it may be confined to single-parent families or foster families. Note that the two main forms or types of family structure usually referred to by scholars are the nuclear family and the extended family. The change from "concepts" to "forms" was linked with the debate regarding paragraph 5.5. The original language from Prep Comm III stated: "Governments should take effective action to eliminate all forms of coercion and discrimination in policies and practices related to marriage, other unions and the family." The Islamic nations, some Latin American and African nations, and the Holy See moved to eliminate "other unions." Some nations proposed the rewording "related to the family," while others argued for "marriage and the family." The opposition, led by the Scandinavian nations and supported by the United States insisted on retaining "other unions." The compromise then was to omit the entire phrase "related to marriage, other unions and the family," and to change "concepts" to "forms" in paragraph 5.1.

Paragraph 5.1 states that "Traditional notions of gender-based division of parental and domestic functions and participation in the paid labor force do not reflect current realities and aspirations, as more and more women in all parts of the world take up paid employment outside the home." While this may be an accurate description of trends, it does not analyze whether this is a desired option for the women or a desirable situation for family life and for society. For many women it is a necessity due to socio-economic conditions. It may not be their choice, nor their long-term commitment. Furthermore, as written, the sentence tends to set paid employment outside the home as the norm, without recognizing the value to family life and self-fulfillment realized by those who do not seek outside work. This is another example of how the *PA* attempts to create new attitudes and values without recognition of all the implications of approving a new or different social trend.

Nonetheless, most of the revised chapter 5 did address the needs of families, and it can be helpful in urging governments to provide help and support for families.

Reproductive Health

In the original drafts chapter 7 dealt with "sexual and reproductive rights," with the intention of including abortion as a reproductive right. The final document uses the title "Reproductive Rights and Reproductive Health." However, chapter 7 was one of the most hotly contested chapters in the *PA*. Its final version was linked to other chapters, especially chapter 8 in regard to abortion. The first paragraph, 7.1, states that the chapter is guided by the principles of chapter 2, and in particular the introductory paragraphs. These recall the UN principle of sovereignty, noting that full respect should be given by each nation to "the various religious and ethical values and cultural backgrounds of its people, and in conformity with universally recognized human rights." While this recognizes religious and ethical values, it is not a strong moral safeguard, especially in nations that have permissive attitudes and laws regarding sexual behavior.

Paragraph 7.2 begins with a definition of reproductive health. It quickly moves to a series of assertions regarding reproductive rights which rest on the "right of men and women to be informed and have access to safe, effective and affordable methods of family planning of their choice, as well as other methods of their choice for regulation of fertility which are not against the law." This is a variation on the common UN formulation that all couples and individuals have the basic right to decide freely and responsibly the number, spacing, and timing of their children and to have the information and means to do so. The language of paragraph 7.2 is vague, but it is an improvement over the language of Prep Comm III, which defined reproductive health as including "fertility regulation," which the World Health Organization (WHO) defined as including abortion. After much debate throughout the entire conference, the words "methods of their choice for regulation of fertility which are not against the law" were accepted. No doubt these methods would include sterilization, but arguably would not automatically include abortion, at least not on the basis of the WHO definition. This new language prevails throughout the rest of the PA. The final sentence of paragraph 7.2 gives a revised and shortened definition of sexual health which is extremely vague.

Both at the Prep Comm Meetings and at Cairo the Holy See attempted to give a clear and precise definition of reproductive health services, and to exclude abortion. The Church throughout the world sponsors or maintains more than 96,000 health care institutions, many in mission countries. Many of these institutions provide primary health care services, especially to women and children. Reproductive health services are important and beneficial to both the mother, the unborn child, and the entire family. Such services would include prenatal education and care, proper care of mother and child during childbirth and during the early months of pregnancy, information on proper nutrition and breast-feeding, protection against infectious disease, and education of men in regard to the father's roles and responsibilities.

The final version of paragraph 7.6 provides a more detailed description of reproductive health services, similar to that provided by the Holy See. But it also includes abortion, with a reference to chapter 8 (par. 8.25), where the language of Mexico City is included, stating that "in no case should abortion be promoted as a method of family planning" (Rec. 18, e). Nonetheless, abortion is accepted in regard to unwanted pregnancies; abortion is left to national laws which differ greatly country by country. There is a tacit presumption in favor of national abortion laws and, without any scientific evidence about abortion incidence, a presumption that safety can and should be assured wherever abortion is legal. This amounts to approval of legally accepted abortion and encouragement of permissive legal structures.

Paragraph 7.3 states that "reproductive rights embrace certain human rights," but it does not name the human rights. It states the common UN formulation regarding the right of couples and individuals to information and methods to plan family size. It goes further in asserting a newly found "right to attain the highest standard of sexual and reproductive health." Further it asserts that these rights "should be the fundamental basis for government and community-supported policies and programmes in the area of reproductive health, including family planning." The final sentences express concern that adolescents and the elderly have special needs in regard to reproductive health services. The entire paragraph is objectionable on moral and ethical grounds, and also because it attempts to assert new rights and entitlements that have never been adopted nor discussed in a United Nations forum.

Paragraph 7.4 was a new paragraph developed in Cairo stating that "the implementation of the present Programme of Action is to be guided by the above comprehensive definition of reproductive health, which includes sexual health." This paragraph clearly defines the intent of this chapter and of the entire *PA*.

Recognizing the importance of reproductive health care, as well as the importance of a proper understanding and evaluation of sexual health, chapter 7 fails to give a framework of values, responsibilities, and strategies that will decrease disease and irresponsible sexual behavior. It attempts to assert new and undefined rights, and thus entitlements and societal obligations, all without any basis in international law or covenants. Furthermore, chapter 7 assumes sexual permissiveness as the norm and avoids any discussion of societal or personal restraint on sexual behavior. While the chapter does not fully endorse abortion on demand and expresses the need for reducing abortion, it still tends towards accepting, if not approving, a more liberal legal approach to abortion.

Abortion

There was a clear intent from the earliest preparatory committee meetings to include abortion as a reproductive right. This intent was promoted by the United States,[10] and shared by many American non-governmental organizations, which wrote the preliminary drafts of the *PA* and by some UN officials. In order to avoid long, difficult, and distracting debates, the European Union drafted an abortion paragraph to be included in chapter 8 and proposed to limit all discussion of abortion to that particular paragraph. Some of those promoting abortion were committed to eliminating any reference to the 1984 Mexico City language urging governments "to take appropriate steps to help women avoid abortion, which in no case should be promoted as a method of family planning, and whenever possible, provide for the humane treatment and counseling of women who have had recourse to abortion" (Rec. 8, e).[11] But in the European Union proposal, the mechanism to reduce recourse to abortion was "expanded and improved family planning services." Paragraph 8.25 goes beyond the 1984 formulation in that it links unwanted pregnancies with safe abortion information and counseling. It also approves the use of national legislation to deal with abortion and to assure the safety of abortion practice. Paragraph 8.25 changes the tone of the Mexico City language from discouraging abortion to tolerating, approving, and improving its safety where it is legal.

The European Union effort to limit the abortion debate to paragraph 8.25 failed, and reference to the Mexico City language was included in paragraphs 7.6 and 7.24. Furthermore, the abortion issue, though sent off to a small working group, remained a problem for the Cairo conference throughout its entire duration,

---

[10] See A. McIntosh and J. Finkle, "The Cairo Conference on Population and Development: A New Paradigm?" *Population and Development Review,* June 1995. This article is a fairly good report of the events and tensions at the Cairo conference. The authors, however, are proposing their own explanation, and there may be disagreement on some aspects of the article.

[11] *Report of the International Conference on Population, 1984* (New York: United Nations, 1984).

right to the final sessions. Moreover, the texts adopted called forth objection and dissent from many nations, and that is appended to the final text. All things considered, the Holy See played an important role in its defense of the language that it had originally introduced in Mexico City in 1984. At the same time, the delegation of Malta was indispensable and provided the tactical leadership both in the Working Group and in the Plenary.

Sexual Freedom

The *PA* asserts an individualistic and highly permissive approach to human sexuality and to the conjugal relationship. This conditions its treatment of the family, of parent-child relations, and of sexual behavior in general. It was the basis of attempting to include sexual rights, completely undefined, as fundamental human rights, and to extend those rights to the unmarried, to adolescents, and to homosexuals and lesbians. Some examples may be helpful.

The so-called "right of couples and individuals" to family planning information and means is present throughout the document. In many instances it is expanded beyond its understanding in the 1974 and 1984 conferences. While the chairman of the Working Committee promised some clarification of the meaning of "individuals," there is no indication that was ever accomplished. Thus the very vagueness of the term, and the unwillingness of leaders of the conference to place some limits on its interpretation, elicited objection and dissent, especially from the Arab and Latin American countries.

Emphasis on providing reproductive and sexual health services to adolescents appears throughout the document, despite the fact that a specific part of chapter 7 (part E) is directed to adolescents. There is little coherence and the many references create confusion and possible dangers. A preoccupation is to provide contraceptive education and services to adolescents so as to enhance sexual freedom and sexual health. So for instance, paragraph 6.7 calls for "access to education, health counselling and high quality services in sexual and reproductive health" to meet the special needs of adolescents and youth, especially young women. Little recognition is given to parents and the need for society to express disapproval of sexual libertarianism and to call for personal discipline and self-restraint. The document fully intends to include unmarried adolescents in the term "individuals," which is crucial for the significance of the statement

146

of the so-called right to information and means to avoid pregnancy. Delegates repeatedly made efforts to draw attention to the rights and responsibilities of parents, drawing from the "Convention on the Rights of the Child" and other UN conventions.

Women's Issues and Feminist Determination

There was an original intent to focus on the role of women in development, a recommendation from the 1984 Mexico City conference. The education of women, equality of status and opportunity in regard to economic realities and employment, health care of women and children, and women's role in the family are important issues in any consideration of population and development. Some of these issues are treated in a general way in chapter 4, "Gender Equality, Equity and the Empowerment of Women." But the original intent was frustrated by the overemphasis on establishing new and undefined "sexual rights," and a universal right to abortion.[12] The roles of women in the development process were overshadowed, and as the document was debated and revised, women's rights were described primarily in terms of the right to sexual freedom, the right to bear children regardless of marriage, the right to contracept, and the right to abort. In this approach, woman is an autonomous individual, free of responsibilities, and without much need for human relationships of a stable or compelling nature, particularly in terms of marriage and family. There was also disagreement among feminist groups about family planning programs, some seeing them as unnecessary, others, as oppressive of women. Moreover, many of the proposed goals reflected the concerns of women in developed nations, very often overlooking the demographic realities and the needs of women in developing nations. Consequently, the Cairo conference lost an opportunity to give a more universal understanding and appreciation of women's roles, potentialities, actual contributions to the good of society, and their specific role in development strategies.

Nonetheless, many left Cairo intending to bring back the sexual and reproductive rights issues at the 1995 international women's conference in Beijing. This attempt was certainly made, but once again failed to achieve its expectations. Sexual orientation was not allowed to replace concern about the family,

---

[12] Ibid. McIntosh and Finkle describe the feminist influence on the *PA* and the concerted efforts of feminist organizations to see their agenda approved.

and abortion was not accepted as a fundamental right in Beijing. Again, the Holy See took part in the Beijing conference and had a moderating influence.[13]

Conclusion

What is to be learned from the participation of the Holy See in the Cairo conference? Many would question whether anything worthwhile was achieved and whether the Catholic Church should ever be involved at all in international conferences dealing with public affairs or political issues.

In light of my personal involvement at all the international population conferences and the regular meetings of the UN Commission on Population and Development, I consider Cairo a successful effort and well-worth repeating.

There was an openness on the part of most nations to hear from the Holy See and in many cases, to join with it in its initiatives, especially in regard to human rights, equality, the family, protection of cultural traditions, social justice, and the role of the United Nations.

The Holy See, because of its constant following of population issues, has developed a certain expertise and is accorded respect when it addresses these issues, especially because of its efforts to relate population to development. The high visibility of Pope John Paul II, the diplomatic contacts, and the statements of many bishops and bishops' conferences were seen as signs of commitment, determination, and appropriate testimony to human and moral values on the part of the Church. Even the criticism is evidence that the Church is acknowledged and respected.

The media coverage was mixed, but to the degree that the Holy See opened itself to and worked with the media, the coverage was generally fair and good.

The agenda of the Cairo conference was a point of confrontation between the United States and the Holy See. By holding to principle the Holy See gained the support of other nations and faced down the power and prestige of the United States and the Clinton Administration.[14]

Where does that take us for the future? We must remember that the involvement of the Church includes the talents and

---

[13] See M.A. Glendon, "What Happened at Beijing," *First Things,* January 1996, pp. 30-36. Glendon led the Holy See's delegation in Beijing.

[14] See McIntosh and Finkle, "Cairo Conference."

abilities of competent lay persons, who at Cairo and Beijing were fully active members of the delegation. Catholic politicians should be held to a knowledge of the Church's positions and to a conscientious adherence to moral principles, not public opinion polls. Bishops and priests must be in the forefront, providing leadership and direction, regardless of criticism, ridicule, and rejection. But we must also provide room for the legitimate fulfillment of the witness and public efforts of the laity.

We live in a complex and sometimes fragmented world. We bring the witness of Christ, of the Church's commitment to moral principle and human values. We have an opportunity and a responsibility to build or shape a consensus among nations for those initiatives consistent with the teaching of the Church as well as their own cultural traditions and policies that respect and support human dignity and the common good, particularly in regard to development, the well-being of the family, the sanctity of human life, and our common moral responsibilities in regard to population growth or decline. We should not fail in this responsibility.

CHAPTER 11

The Encyclical Letter
Evangelium vitae:
What Are the New Elements?

THE MOST REVEREND ELIO SGRECCIA

The Origins of the Document

The Roman historian Polybius wrote that in order to reconstruct the origins of an historical event, one needs to examine not only the immediate cause, which he calls the "*prophasis*," but also the real or actual cause, which he calls "*aitia*," and the ultimate or remote cause, the "*arche.*"

If we wanted to apply this paradigm to the origin of this document, which certainly represents an important historical standpoint, we would have to say that the immediate situation is constituted by a nearly unanimous vote, which the cardinals, assembled for an exceptional consistory in April of 1991, presented to the Holy Father. Precisely at the end of this meeting, which was dedicated to the problem of offenses and acts of human violence in the world, the pope was asked to publish a document of the highest doctrinal and pastoral significance on the theme of respect for life from conception until death.

This article appeared originally in Italian as "*L'Enciclica* Evangelium Vitae*: quale novità?" Medicina e morale* 4 (August 1995), 655-675. It is translated here by Leslie Raffay, Department of Romance Languages, Harvard University.

This vote was received by the Holy Father and, at the beginning of Pentecost, a form of inquiry was sent to all the bishops around the world together with a letter from the secretary of state. The letter was accompanied by a questionnaire for gathering data on the situation of each diocese and an opinion on the pastoral action to be carried out.

The attained responses were examined, and through the will of John Paul II, the first draft of the document, which has had various revisions, was carried out under the direct responsibility and participation of the Holy Father himself. The publication date (March 25) is significant because it coincides with the Feast of the Annunciation, the glad announcement of the Incarnation, of the divine life that is given to all of humanity.

But the circumstance that has given origin to the encyclical supposes, in turn, a more profound causality than the situation itself of abandonment and offense of human life in various forms, in all parts of the world, and in diverse phases of human existence.

In its time, this situation originates from a mentality, from a culture of death that has its roots in the development of modern and contemporary thought and has found expression in true and actual "structures of sin." It is for this reason that the theme of the protection of life is presented by the Holy Father as the "new social question," no less crucial than the one that was proposed at the time of Leo XIII, the labor question.[1]

This more profound analysis of the situation and of the culture of death is developed in the first chapter of the encyclical.

The Voice of Your Brother's Blood Cries to Me from the Ground

This part of the encyclical can be defined as an extensive and profound analysis of the offenses and the acts of violence that are carried out against human life in such a serious and extensive way for the first time in the history of humanity.

The chapter opens with the title drawn from the biblical story of Cain and Abel: "The voice of your brother's blood cries to me from the ground" (Gen. 4:2-16).

The biblical passage is reread in present terms, in all of its fratricidal dramatic force, in its ties with the Evil One, who "was a murderer from the beginning" (John 8:44), in the consequent

[1] John Paul II, *Evangelium vitae* (March 25, 1995), 5 (hereafter cited in the body of the text as *EV* with section numbers).

crime full of violence and envy, which was followed by God's call ("Where is your brother Abel?"), and the indifferent response ("I do not know; am I my brother's keeper?") (Gen. 4:9), and the final remorse of Cain, to whom God grants protection anyway, so that even the life of Cain is protected from violence. God cannot leave the sin unpunished, but he does not want revenge to break out unrestrained onto the life of the guilty one: "'God, who preferred the correction rather than the death of a sinner, did not desire that a homicide be punished by the exaction of another act of homicide'[2]" (*EV,* 9).

The encyclical, nevertheless, points out not only the vastness and multiplicity of the offenses against human life due to poverty–negligence in the prevention of natural disasters, wars and collective violence, and above all, voluntary abortion and euthanasia–but it also urgently warns that in our era some crimes, particularly against the birth and death of a life,

> present *new characteristics with respect to the past and which raise questions of extraordinary seriousness.* It is not only that in generalized opinion these attacks tend no longer to be considered as "crimes"; paradoxically they assume the nature of "rights", to the point that the State is called upon to give them *legal recognition and to make them available through the free services of health-care personnel.* Such attacks strike human life at the time of its greatest frailty, when it lacks any means of self-defence. Even more serious is the fact that, most often, those attacks are carried out in the very heart of and with the complicity of the family–the family which by its nature is called to be the "sanctuary of life". (*EV,* 11)

This passage from crime to right is expressed in the legalization of abortion and euthanasia.

The Holy Father speaks of the "structure of sin," of the "conspiracy against life," and of the "war of the powerful against the weak." In confirmation of this fact, *Evangelium vitae* (13) cites the political and planned organization of the reduction of births in worldwide scope, the setting up of new strategies for abortive contraception–a point to which we will return–the diffusion of artificial reproductive techniques, prenatal diagnosis with preselective intentions, and euthanasia of the terminally ill. In

[2] In this passage, *EV* quotes Saint Ambrose, *De Cain et Abel,* II, 10, 38; *Corpus Scriptorum Ecclesiasticorum Latinorum,* 32, 408.

152

particular, the pope points out this new fact connected with the population problem.

> In the face of overpopulation in the poorer countries, instead of forms of global intervention at the international level–serious family and social policies, programmes of cultural development and of fair production and distribution of resources–anti-birth policies continue to be enacted. (*EV*, 16)

The encyclical denounces the recourse to the planning of contraceptive practices, abortion and sterilization directed towards solving the population problem, and compares those responsible for such politics to the pharaoh of Egypt, who commanded the extermination of male babies born into Jewish families.

After this overall look at negative circumstances for human life in the world, the encyclical proposes an examination of the causes.

There are, substantially, four causes that the Holy Father considers as the basis of this conspiracy against life, which develops itself, paradoxically, in an era of proclamation of human rights, and in clear contradiction to these rights, it negates the most fundamental one, the right to life.

The encyclical makes reference first of all to the secularization of a culture. Many segments of contemporary culture have lost the meaning of God and have come to lose also the meaning of humanity. This diagnosis has already been proposed by the Second Vatican Ecumenical Council in the Pastoral Constitution *Gaudium et spes* (36). "*When the sense of God is lost, there is also a tendency to lose the sense of man*, of his dignity and his life" (*EV*, 21). Within this picture of impoverishment and loss of sense, moral disorder–which consists in the separating of liberty from truth–is suggested as the related cause.

> When freedom is made absolute in an individualistic way, it is emptied of its original content, and its very meaning and dignity are contradicted.
>
> ...Freedom negates and destroys itself, and becomes a factor leading to the destruction of others, when it no longer recognizes and respects *its essential link with the truth.* (*EV*, 19)

This separation "*leads to a serious distortion of life in society*" (*EV*, 20). In order to avoid the struggle and the dispute over selfish interests, one goes so far as to propose ethical contractualism.

> At that point, *everything is negotiable, everything is open to bargaining:* even the first of the fundamental rights, the right to life.
> ...In this way democracy, contradicting its own principles, effectively moves towards a form of totalitarianism. The State is no longer the "common home" where all can live together on the basis of principles of fundamental equality, but is transformed into a *tyrant State,* which arrogates to itself the right to dispose of the life of the weakest and most defenceless members, from the unborn child to the elderly, in the name of a public interest which is really nothing but the interest of one part." (*EV*, 20)

In this part, the encyclical contains one of its strongest passages that has provoked more than resentment in the liberal and radical press. The word of the pope does not bend to diplomatic circumlocution:

> To claim the right to abortion, infanticide and euthanasia, and to recognize that right in law, means to attribute to human freedom a *perverse and evil significance:* that of an *absolute power over others and against others.* This is the death of true freedom. (*EV*, 20)

Another even more interesting cultural reason that pertains to the modern era is mentioned by the encyclical when it speaks, still in this part, about a dichotomy, in anthropological terms, already begun at the time of rationalist dualism. The human subject is defined only in relation to rationality, pulled out of context of his or her nature and corporeity.

This has had, in recent times, the consequence of considering "as a subject of rights only the person who enjoys full or at least incipient autonomy and who emerges from a state of total dependence on others" or even, who is led "to *equate personal dignity with the capacity for verbal and explicit,* or at least perceptible, *communication*" (*EV*, 19).

The consequences of this cultural attitude, already revealed in the encyclical *Veritatis splendor* and even in the *Letter to Families,* are numerous: the consideration of corporeity as something extrinsic to an individual, not being a part of his or her identity, and considered, therefore, as an object. And from this, an impoverishment of corporeity, of sexuality, and of interpersonal relations is also derived (*EV*, 23). This analysis of the contemporary anthropological crisis has been done, also among others, by R. Spaemann who affirms:

> When man wants to be only a subject and forgets his symbiotic ties with nature, he falls prisoner to a primitive destiny....In order to survive and live well, it is necessary that people act in a proper manner, not only some with regard to others, but also with regard to their own nature and to an external nature.[3]

In the end, what is derived from this exasperated exaltation of the subject is moral relativism, and what the encyclical defines as "an *extremely serious and mortal danger:* that of *confusion between good and evil,* precisely in relation to the fundamental right to life" (*EV*, 24).

These pages of historical philosophical analysis of modern and contemporary culture present an element of profound penetration and novel passages, which merit being pointed out.

The chapter concludes with an opening to hope, the hope anticipated by the Risen Christ with His victory over death, the hope that is confirmed even today by those signs that the Holy Father calls "the signs of hope" present and alive in the proof of so many married couples, in the initiatives for the support and development of families (even, and above all, those stricken with poverty, illness, drugs and AIDS), in the fervor of so many movements and centers for assisting life, and in the activities in support of even the most fragile situations.

Among the mentioned signs of hope are also the centers for bioethics and an ever more growing sensitivity against war and the use of force, and finally, the affirmations of ecological sensibility.

This first part concludes with an appeal to "the inescapable responsibility of *choosing to be unconditionally pro-life*" (*EV*, 28).

I Came That They May Have Life

This part of the encyclical is profoundly theological, pervaded, that is, by a theology that is highly contemplative and

[3] R. Spaemann, *Per la cultura dell'utopia politica* (Milan: F. Angeli, 1994), p. 20.

motivating at the same time, and that presents itself with a distinctly original approach.

In order to present the value of human life, the encyclical starts with the evangelical announcement of divine life given to man with the Incarnation, Death, and Resurrection of Christ. It is from this gift of divine life that human life becomes, even in the earthly phase, more precious, elevated and of "almost divine" worth, as the text explains.

The approach that we can expect is analogous to documents with an introduction on scientific facts and development of arguments of a philosophic nature. Here, the given rationale is not overlooked; in fact, many times it is confirmed that the value of life "*can also be known in its essential traits by human reason*" (*EV*, 29), but the anthropology of this encyclical starts from Christology and it is strongly and substantially tied with it.

> In Jesus, the "Word of life", God's eternal life is thus proclaimed and given. Thanks to this proclamation and gift, our physical and spiritual life, also in its earthly phase, acquires its full value and meaning, for God's eternal life is in fact the end to which our living in this world is directed and called. In this way the *Gospel of life* includes everything that human experience and reason tell us about the value of human life, accepting it, purifying it, exalting it and bringing it to fulfilment. (*EV*, 30)

This fact appears to me to be in accordance with the theology of John Paul II (since the setting forth of his first encyclical, *Redemptor hominis*), and presents very interesting results, from an epistemological point of view, with regard to the relationship between reason and faith (to which we will return later). Reason and faith are not like two parallel lines, or two separate sources, but faith illuminates reason from within, and reason becomes elevated and brought into depths of vision through faith.

The scriptural excursus with which the value of human life is reread, that it is "*the object of God's gentle and intense love*" (*EV*, 31), begins with creation and ends with a call to the beatific vision, maintaining the center of its richness in Christ, dead and risen.

Life is always a privilege, therefore, because it is endowed with spirituality and transcendence, because the divine breath of the spirit pervades it, and because it is derived from God the Creator and is called upon to participate as the child of God.

Here the Christian truth about life becomes most sublime. The dignity of this life is linked not only to its beginning, to the fact that it comes from God, but also to its final end, to its destiny of fellowship with God in knowledge and love of him. In the light of this truth Saint Irenaeus qualifies and completes his praise of man: "the glory of God" is indeed, "man, living man", but "the life of man consists in the vision of God".[4] (*EV,* 38)

This theandric vision of human life gives rise to several principles of consequence: God alone is master of human life. He cares for and is attentive to it (*EV,* 39); human life is sacred and inviolable, and the commandment of the decalogue expresses a truth inscribed in the heart of man, right from the beginning (*EV,* 40). The responsibility that is entrusted to man when facing human life not only deals with not killing, but also, in a positive sense, with respect, veneration and love towards one's fellow man. Such responsibility is reflected in the processes of procreation, which involve the transmission of the image of God to a new creature (*EV,* 43), and also extends itself, with due ontological and axiological distinction, to the lives of other living beings, who are at the service of people and, at the same time, are entrusted with the care and protection of people.

At this point, the thought of the encyclical leads to the reaffirmation of the personal value of newborn human life, the affirmation of veneration for the sick and the elderly and, in general, towards physical existence.

> Certainly *the life of the body in its earthly state is not an absolute good* for the believer, especially as he may be asked to give up his life for a greater good. As Jesus says: "Whoever would save his life will lose it; and whoever loses his life for my sake and the gospel's will save it" (*Mk* 8:35)....
>
> No one, however, can arbitrarily choose whether to live or die; the absolute master of such a decision is the Creator alone, in whom "we live and move and have our being" (*Acts* 17:28). (*EV,* 47)

The gospel of life also includes the meaning of human life: It is a gift that is given in order to be given. Christ's cross expresses the profound meaning of life, which is given up for love and opened up to the resurrection. The last sections (50-51) of this

---

[4] "*Vita autem hominis visio Dei*": *Adversus Haereses,* IV, 20, 7: *SCh* 100/2, 648-649.

second part are dedicated, however, "to *contemplate the One who was pierced*....By his death, Jesus sheds light on the meaning of the life and death of every human being" (*EV,* 50).

You Shall Not Kill

The third part of the encyclical condenses the ethical aspects of the protection of human life and also touches on, with new points and politically relevant interests, the great problem of the relation between moral law and civil law.

The chapter begins with a premise of theological-biblical nature, and an explanation of an ethical nature.

The premise of theological-biblical nature refers to the importance of the commandment "Do not kill."

> As explicitly formulated, the precept "You shall not kill" is strongly negative: it indicates the extreme limit which can never be exceeded. Implicitly, however, it encourages a positive attitude of absolute respect for life; it leads to the promotion of life and to progress along the way of a love which gives, receives and serves. (*EV,* 54)

The second premise consists of an examination of those cases that are usually adopted as exceptions to the principle of "do not kill" and which, in reality, strengthen such an obligation and are aligned with it. It deals with the concept of legitimate defense and with capital punishment (*EV,* 55-56).

At this point the encyclical inserts three pronouncements, which constitute the strongest doctrinal part of the document.

These are not matters of dogmatic definitions *ex cathedra,* because they are found in a document of ordinary teaching, but they contain the same vigor and, in some measure, the same form.

The first pronouncement regards the killing of an innocent person. In *Evangelium vitae* (57) it is affirmed that "the absolute inviolability of innocent human life is a moral truth clearly taught by Sacred Scripture, constantly upheld in the Church's tradition and consistently proposed by her Magisterium."

It is in the strength of this affirmation that the consequent theologically qualified and committed enunciation is formulated:

> Therefore, by the authority which Christ conferred upon Peter and his Successors, and in communion with the

Bishops of the Catholic Church, *I confirm that the direct and voluntary killing of an innocent human being is always gravely immoral.* This doctrine, based uon that unwritten law which man, in the light of reason, finds in his own heart (cf. *Rom* 2:14-15), is reaffirmed by Sacred Scripture, transmitted by the Tradition of the Church and taught by the ordinary and universal Magisterium. (*EV*, 57)

As one can observe, it is a matter of *moral truth,* and with that, I think the encyclical wants to respond to those who object that definitions of theological character must always apply to dogmatic truth and not to moral precepts that would be of a strictly applicative nature. Here, it speaks of truth also in the moral arena, because the moral contains a truth, and the Church is competent also in this aspect, which is connected with salvation.

The second pronouncement regards procured abortion. Procured abortion is not explicitly listed among the crimes and sins within Holy Scripture, precisely because such a practice was not conceivable during the time when Holy Scripture was composed. Instead, Holy Scripture speaks abundantly of the protection and the dominion of God over the human being "as far back as the mother's womb."[5] The pronouncement affirms that this moral truth concerning the prohibition of abortion is "based upon the natural law and upon the written Word of God" and "transmitted by the Church's Tradition" (*EV*, 62).

After having acknowledged the continual testimony of the Pontiffs and teaching of the Church in relation to abortion, the Holy Father expresses the following in the encyclical:

Therefore, by the authority which Christ conferred upon Peter and his Successors, in communion with the Bishops–who on various occasions have condemned abortion and who in the aforementioned consultation, albeit dispersed throughout the world, have shown unanimous agreement concerning this doctrine–*I declare that direct abortion, that is, abortion willed as an end or as a means, always constitutes a grave moral disorder,* since it is the deliberate killing of an innocent human being. This doctrine is based upon the natural law and upon the written Word of God, is transmitted by the Church's Tradition and taught by the ordinary and universal Magisterium. (*EV*, 62)

[5] Psalm 139/8 and other passages.

The encyclical then concentrates on considering some of the consequences derived from this moral truth; first of all, with regard to experimentation on the embryo.

> Although "one must uphold as licit procedures carried out on the human embryo which respect the life and integrity of the embryo and do not involve disproportionate risks for it, but rather are directed to its healing, the improvement of its condition of health, or its individual survival",[6] it must nonetheless be stated that the use of human embryos or fetuses as an object of experimentation constitutes a crime against their dignity as human beings who have a right to the same respect owed to a child once born, just as to every person. (*EV*, 63)

Experimentation upon early embryos can, in fact, compromise the genome of that embryo which, in turn, can have consequences upon posterity, with serious mutational risks for the subject's lineage.

The moral condemnation extends to the practice of drawing tissues and organs derived from live embryos in order to cure diseases.

The encyclical refers, finally, to the condemnation of the use of prenatal diagnosis with the intention of selective abortion.

The third pronouncement concerns euthanasia. It offers a clear definition: "*Euthanasia in the strict sense* is understood to be an action or omission which of itself and by intention causes death, with the purpose of eliminating all suffering" (*EV*, 65). The encyclical refers to the *Declaration on Euthanasia* by the Sacred Congregation for the Doctrine of the Faith (1980) and clarifies the distinction between euthanasia and the decision to avoid so-called "aggressive medical treatment" (*EV*, 65). This is understood as any intervention that worsens the condition of the patient without being truly effective, or one that in any way involves a serious disproportion between the positive results and an increase in the suffering of the patient and family members. Concerning euthanasia, here is the theologically binding formula:

> Taking into account these distinctions, in harmony with the Magisterium of my Predecessors and in communion with the

---

[6] Congregation for the Doctrine of the Faith, *Instruction on Respect for Human Life in its Origin and on the Dignity of Procreation* (*Donum vitae*), February 22, 1987, I, 3; *Acta Apostolicae Sedis* 80 (1988), 80.

Bishops of the Catholic Church, *I confirm that euthanasia is a grave violation of the law of God,* since it is the deliberate and morally unacceptable killing of a human person. This doctrine is based upon the natural law and upon the written Word of God, is transmitted by the Church's Tradition and taught by the ordinary and universal Magisterium. (*EV*, 65)

The teaching of the encyclical continues to make explicit the reasons for condemning not only homicide, but also suicide, including the recently proposed form of "assisted suicide." Passing then to a positive outlook towards the dying, inspired by the "*way of love and true mercy*" (*EV*, 67), the encyclical gives an ethical and pastoral profile of assistance to the dying, founded on participation in the mystery of Christ's Death and Resurrection, in communion with "living and dying for the Lord". It also recalls means of assistance directed towards relieving suffering (palliative care) and at providing integrated assistance, human and spiritual.

In this same chapter, beginning from section 68, one encounters a new theme, full of consequences at the level of political and civil debate, and that is the theme of the relationship between moral law and civil law.

This part of the encyclical has provoked immediate discussions and will involve many more to come. There is still room for further examination in this field. The encyclical mentions that moral law does not have the same area of competence that civil law has, because moral law regards all human acts, even internal ones, whereas civil law regards the common good; nevertheless, civil law cannot legalize acts against the fundamental values of a person and of its own society. We can summarize this teaching in the following statements:

(a) The pretenses of legal justification for abortion and euthanasia cannot be accepted with the proportionalist motive of the balancing of opposing values in society, and not even with the motive of adaptation at the level of experienced morality, or making an appeal to the radical demands of individual autonomy, all of which are theories inspired by ethical relativism. The laws that are enacted against life assume a tyrannical and antidemocratic aspect. The Church, which in various documents has indicated democracy as the best form of government and even a "sign of the times," denounces the distortions of this system:

The value of democracy stands or falls with the values which it embodies and promotes. Of course, values such as the dignity of every human person, respect for inviolable and inalienable human rights, and the adoption of the "common good" as the end and criterion regulating political life are certainly fundamental and not to be ignored. (*EV*, 70)

Therefore,

Civil law must ensure that all members of society enjoy respect for certain fundamental rights which innately belong to the person, rights which every positive law must recognize and guarantee. First and fundamental among these is the inviolable right to life of every innocent human being. While public authority can sometimes choose not to put a stop to something which—were it prohibited—would cause more serious harm, it can never presume to legitimize as a right of individuals—even if they are the majority of the members of society—an offence against other persons caused by the disregard of so fundamental a right as the right to life. The legal toleration of abortion or euthanasia can in no way claim to be based on respect for the conscience of others, precisely because society has the right and the duty to protect itself against the abuses which can occur in the name of conscience and under the pretext of freedom. (*EV*, 71)

(b) On the basis of the principle always recognized in the Church's doctrine, inferred from its natural and rational foundation, civil law can never be opposed to moral law; when that would happen, civil law "is not really a law but rather a corruption of the law."[7] Therefore,

Laws which authorize and promote abortion and euthanasia are therefore radically opposed not only to the good of the individual but also to the common good; as such they are completely lacking in authentic juridical validity. (*EV*, 72)

(c) In consequence, the encyclical proposes the duty of conscientious objection. "There is no obligation in conscience to obey such laws; instead there is a *grave and clear obligation to oppose them by conscientious objection*" (*EV*, 73). Conscientious objection pertains to every action that by its nature, or by the character it assumes in a concrete context, qualifies as participation in an act

[7] Saint Thomas Aquinas, *Summa Theologiae*, I-II, q. 95, a. 2, as quoted in *EV*, 72.

against innocent human life or as a share in the immoral intention of the principal agent.

> In this sense, the opportunity to refuse to take part in the phases of consultation, preparation and execution of these acts against life should be guaranteed to physicians, health-care personnel, and directors of hospitals, clinics and convalescent facilities. Those who have recourse to conscientious objection must be protected not only from legal penalties but also from any negative effects on the legal, disciplinary, financial and professional plane. (*EV*, 74)

(d) The encyclical examines what is defined as a "particular problem of conscience" and regards cases

> where a legislative vote would be decisive for the passage of a more restrictive law, aimed at limiting the number of authorized abortions, in place of a more permissive law already passed or ready to be voted on. Such cases are not infrequent....In a case like the one just mentioned, when it is not possible to overturn or completely abrogate a pro-abortion law, an elected official, whose absolute personal opposition to procured abortion was well known, could licitly support proposals aimed at *limiting the harm* done by such a law and at lessening its negative consequences at the level of general opinion and public morality. This does not in fact represent an illicit cooperation with an unjust law, but rather a legitimate and proper attempt to limit its evil aspects. (*EV*, 73)

(e) In addition to conscientious objection founded on the precept "do not kill," there is and remains the obligation to commit oneself socially with a unity of actions and positive strategies (exempted from violence) towards promoting a new culture and civilization. Civil involvement, in a positive sense, is strongly recommended as a responsibility by the encyclical.

> The commandment "You shall not kill" thus establishes the point of departure for the start of true freedom. It leads us to promote life actively, and to develop particular ways of thinking and acting which serve life. In this way we exercise our responsibility towards the persons entrusted to us and we show, in deeds and in truth our gratitude to God for the great gift of life (cf. *Ps* 139:13-14). (*EV*, 76)

We are asked to love and honour the life of every man and woman and to work with perseverance and courage so that our time, marked by all too many signs of death, may at last witness the establishment of a new culture of life, the fruit of the culture of truth and of love. (*EV*, 77)

You Did It to Me

The fourth part of the Encyclical contains a pastoral plan for however many feel they belong to the "community of the people of life."

Such a plan begins with a deep conviction that concerns the same theme of the encyclical: the defense of human life and its dignity are a part of the gospel itself.

Therefore, it is not the task of some "movement" or respectable voluntary association, but it is the responsibility of all believers.

> Evangelization is an all-embracing, progressive activity through which the Church participates in the prophetic, priestly and royal mission of the Lord Jesus. It is therefore inextricably linked to *preaching, celebration and the service of charity....*
>
> This is also the case with regard to the proclamation of the *Gospel of life*, an integral part of that Gospel which is Jesus Christ himself. (*EV*, 78)

In line with this concept, the encyclical speaks of three tasks: evangelize, celebrate, serve life.

Within this plan all the work of formation of conscience takes place. It is turned over to everyone, but in a particular way to health care workers (a phrase that also includes administrators, pharmacists, medical assistants, nurse's aides), legislators and faithful families themselves. As a new initiative the encyclical cites, among other things, the celebration of a "day of life." In short, old and new initiatives of voluntary action and incentive find space within the scope of service, which the Church has already put into progress with dynamism and creativity: centers of life assistance, in-home assistance to the dying and palliative care, assistance in increasing the value of life of the elderly, help to the weakest.

In the conclusion of the encyclical, there is full justification for the prayer to the Virgin Mary, Mother of the Savior, considered as example of life, as custodian of the life of the Son of God made man, and as intercessor opposite the strength of united forces from the culture of death.

What Are the New Elements?

Only a superficial evaluation could support the opinion that the encyclical would not have anything new to say and that, if anything, it would only be valid within the Catholic Church.

I will limit myself to offering a few elements of reflection on the importance of this document.

The first particular element brought to light is represented by the connection, made explicit by the text itself (*EV, 5*), between this encyclical and that of Leo XIII of 1891 on the question of workers, *Rerum novarum*.

The reason for this approach resides in the fact that both encyclicals touch on a subject that is important in a social and worldwide context (not a question of private morals), which is to have future repercussions in the century to come, and, in addition, both encyclicals bear witness to the defense made by the Church in favor of the weakest areas of humanity. This assertion, not made in a rhetorical way, must involve a unity of initiatives, movements of thought and political actions, as occurred analogously in the Catholic world after the publication of *Rerum novarum*.

The analogy is reinforced by our current situation: what is happening now in the world is no less serious or urgent than what happened then, at the end of the last century. It would suffice to recall some of the figures with regard to legalized abortions, exploited and commercialized children, victims of euthanasia, of drugs, of AIDS, of imposed family planning.

One must not be afraid to define this problem as an emergency of worldwide and historically exceptional proportions. It is the problem that the year 2000 is faced with.

Another new element in *Evangelium vitae* is epistemological in character and regards the reasoning outlined inherently in the encyclical. It is easy to notice that, unlike the great social encyclicals—in which reasoning begins with social facts and with rational concepts and motives, in order to then be confirmed with the evidence of faith—this encyclical provides, first of all, the supernatural vision of faith, the gospel's message of the value of human life, seen and considered within the scope of divine life. In a second moment, within this vision, an appeal is made to reason and to the natural law.

We find ourselves facing the message of the *fides quaerens intellectum* more than that of the *intellectus quaerens fidem*.

This shifting or inversion of reasoning is not without motive, in my opinion, and is not without consequences.

First of all, faith is not to be regarded as pleonastic or secondary among the community of believers, a view of faith inducing an attenuation of involvement in the Church itself. The complete vision of the value of life comes to us from the vision of faith.

In second place, this fact teaches us to consider the point of view of faith such that it does not cancel out, nor juxtapose itself to reason, but rather it illuminates and transforms reason from within, according to what Saint Thomas teaches, who reminds us that grace *non destruit sed perficit naturam.* It is the same intellectual faculty to be elevated, invested with supernatural light, according to the principle of the Incarnation and Redemption.

However, the value of life is part of the gospel of the salvation of mankind, and it is perceivable by reason, but in its totality, it is better perceived by reason enlightened with faith. This fact, on the pastoral level, means that the Church cannot consider commitment to life as a peripheral concern, but as essential as the gospel is essential; it also implies that the inviolability of all life, to be sure, but personal human life in particular, is knowable by the light of human reason.

Another new theme of a general nature in the encyclical is suggested by the cultural perspectives that it tends to and points out implicitly.

It discusses the need for our culture to reconstruct some "bridges." The bridge material has an essential and typical function for our life activities. The first structures that were reconstructed after the last war were bridges, precisely so that life could resume itself again.

The bridges that are suggested (even if implicitly) by the encyclical are as follows:

(a) *The bridge between reason and faith.* It is singular and significant that in the three theological statements, the most demanding, in almost dogmatic terms, always refers, together with

Holy Scripture and the teaching of tradition, to the value of reason and the natural law.

And in further passages it recalls how the gospel of life is recognizable also by human reason. We must go beyond the past, which opened itself up to glorification of the Enlightenment ideals and subjective relativism, in order to rediscover a point of contact: a faith that does not neglect reason and a type of reason that remains open to faith and is not prejudicially closed to transcendence. It is a matter of a great and new cultural way, at the worldwide level, towards a new form of civilization.

(b) *The bridge between the person and nature.* It is in sections 19 and 20 of the encyclical, as was said, that the break between the subjectivity of a person and his or her nature is denounced as a characteristic of modernity, and it is on the basis of this fact that the obliteration or the reification of corporeity and sexuality determines itself. The encyclical insists, then, upon a respect for nature, not only that nature which is external to a person, for which the person is a custodian, but also, and foremost, the internal nature that is not only composed of corporeity, but that expresses itself in corporeity. It is in this context that an ontological reading of sexuality is also required. The sexuality of a person is revealed through corporeity: the significance is manifested in the sign, and the sign is ontologically significant when it deals with the body.

This means that one cannot imagine normal sexuality that is not expressed in corporeity and one cannot think of a separation between physical "sex" and "gender," where the gender would indicate a psycho-social dimension different from the physical one.

This nature-person bridge, if one considers nature in the full sense, can contribute to inaugurating a new civilization and a new culture.

(c) *The bridge between civil and moral law.* This particular aspect of the encyclical is discussed in chapter 3.

We have already mentioned this. A civil law cannot be founded without respect for fundamental values of the ethical order, or without the common good. When civil law separates itself from this foundation or opposes it, it provokes trauma in society, an upset in the lives of individuals, and a disturbance in social life.

Conscientious objection is a safeguard for the individual person, and is also a prophetic appeal, but not the complete solution to the problem. The complete solution is to restore to the law its foundation of rationality and its non-opposition to fundamental values.

Other culturally and ethically indispensable bridges can also be identified, such as the bridge between freedom and responsibility and the bridge between ethics as a science of principles and ethics as virtuous behavior.

There are also other new elements in the encyclical that are truly unique and had never been taken into consideration by an official document of the Church.

One such instance is the section dedicated to abortifacient contraceptives[8] and also the paragraph dedicated to problems connected with population growth, a problem that serves as a cover-up for the anti-birth campaigns at a worldwide level and for which contraception, abortion, and sterilization are no longer only individual and private problems of morality, but social and political problems as well.[9]

Now, a prediction: I do not believe that this encyclical will suffer the fate that the press reserves for many documents of the Church, that is, to undergo the conspiracy of silence. As the gospel will be cried out from the roof tops, so this "great cry and lamentation" of the new Rachel, "who cries for her children who are no longer," will make itself heard as far as the ends of the earth.

[8] "In order to facilitate the spread of *abortion,* enormous sums of money have been invested and continue to be invested in the production of pharmaceutical products which make it possible to kill the fetus in the mother's womb without recourse to medical assistance. On this point, scientific research itself seems to be almost exclusively preoccupied with developing products which are ever more simple and effective in suppressing life and which at the same time are capable of removing abortion from any kind of control or social responsibility" (*EV,* 13).

[9] "Another present-day *phenomenon,* frequently used to justify threats and attacks against life, is the *demographic* question....In the face of overpopulation in the poorer countries, instead of global intervention at the international level—serious family and social policies, programmes of cultural development and of fair production and distribution of resources—anti-birth policies continue to be enacted.

"Contraception, sterilization and abortion are certainly part of the reason why in some cases there is a sharp decline in the birthrate. It is not difficult to be tempted to use the same methods and attacks against life also where there is a situation of 'demographic explosion'.

"The Pharaoh of old, haunted by the presence and increase of the children of Israel, submitted them to every kind of oppression and ordered that every male child born of the Hebrew women was to be killed (cf. *Ex* 1:7-22). Today not a few of the powerful of the earth act in the same way. They too are haunted by the current demographic growth, and fear that the most prolific and poorest peoples represent a threat for the well-being and peace of their own countries. Consequently, rather than wishing to face and solve these serious problems with respect for the dignity of individuals and families and for every person's inviolable right to life, they prefer to promote and impose by whatever means a massive programme of birth control. Even the economic help which they would be ready to give is unjustly made conditional on the acceptance of an anti-birth policy" (*EV,* 16).

However, it is not even foreseeable that the solution to the problem is simple or immediate. The Easter battle between death and life (*mors et vita duello conflixere mirando*) however, is won: *dux vitae mortuus regnat vivus.*[10]

---

[10] From the Easter Mass.

CHAPTER 12

From the *Gift* to the *Gospel* of Life: A Theological Interpretation of *Evangelium vitae*

THE REVEREND IGNAZIO CARRASCO DE PAULA

At least eight years after the publication of the *Instruction on Respect for Human Life in Its Origin and on the Dignity of Procreation* (*Donum vitae*[1]) by the Congregation for the Doctrine of Faith, Pope John Paul II has taken up again the same line of discourse with a second and larger document—this time an encyclical, *Evangelium vitae*—concentrating on the value and the inviolability of human life. Both pontifical documents touch on questions of great immediacy and importance for medical ethics, in a line that reconnects them with Hippocratic rationality and, naturally, with Christian tradition. The two texts, however, diverge, in an extremely significant way, not only in the purpose that they intend to reach, but also for the perspective adopted in examining their common theme, human life. For this reason, it seemed fitting to develop these reflections starting with a comparison between the two documents.

This article appeared originally in Italian as "*Dal* dono *al* vangelo *della vita: per una lettura teologica dell' Enciclica* Evangelium Vitae," *Medicina e morale* 4 (August 1995): 757-769. It is translated here by Leslie Raffay, Department of Romance Languages, Harvard University.

[1] February 22, 1987, *Acta Apostolicae Sedis* 80 (1988) 70-102. Hereafter this will be cited as *DV* with section numbers. Similarly, *Evangelium vitae* will hereafter be cited as *EV*.

From *Donum vitae* to *Evangelium vitae*

As one will recall, *Donum vitae* explains, in concise dialogue form, the response of the Church to some moral questions raised by the techniques of artificial reproduction, by genetic research, by prenatal medicine, etc. The instruction explains to what degree and why the new biomedical procedures are or are not consistent with the principles of Catholic morality. Therefore, the field remains focused on the beginning phase of human existence and, in the end, it addresses only two essential questions: On the one hand, what is the ethical attitude to maintain with regard to the human embryo in the different phases of intrauterine growth? On the other hand, which rules should medical intervention in human procreation observe if it wishes to be respectful of the dignity of the person?

The instruction gives a precise response to these two questions. In the first case, the embryo must be treated as a person, from the moment of conception, and therefore, fundamental rights that are inherent in the human species must be recognized. In the second case, the only context worthy of the procreation of a human being is in a conjugal act of love, through which a married couple expresses their mutual donation and sets up the conditions for the conception of a child; as a consequence, medical intervention cannot substitute for a conjugal union, rather, it must assist it, so that it reaches its natural ends.

Eight years later, the problems examined by *Donum vitae* have remained almost unchanged, or if anything, have been made more acute by some extravagant experiences (such as cloning), and by the multiplication of procedures that lack the conditions to be acceptable alternatives for the cure of sterility. Meanwhile, laboratory research has not offered anything new that would modify ethical judgment, yet the debate surrounding the identity of the human embryo seems to cease when it comes to attempts to authorize basic experimentation during the first two weeks of embryonic development; attempts which the instruction of the Congregation for the Doctrine of Faith rejects in the most absolute way.

For What Reasons, then, a New Pontifical Document in Defense of Life?

There seem to be two reasons: one is strictly related to medical ethics, the other is dependent on social and cultural circumstances. The first is established by the creeping return of euthanasia. The right to assisted suicide has already had its first referendum recognition in the state of Oregon (United States of America), the enactment of which has remained suspended for the time being. Meanwhile, the possibility of anticipating the death of the incurably ill, or the elderly who are not self-sufficient, has become a reality in Holland after the approval of an administrative procedure that leaves an ample margin of legal immunity to the doctor who decides to administer a lethal injection to a patient. All of this comes at a very delicate time for the medical profession, a time in which a debate at the worldwide level is taking place regarding the reduction and rationalization of health expeditures. By now, it is well known that, among the areas of study, in more and more places there is discussion of excluding some of the ill, especially the elderly, from access to more expensive therapies, which is already happening regularly in some industrialized nations.

The second reason appears to be much more complex. It arises from the recognition that certain aggressive measures against life selectively attack the most defenseless subjects, such as children and the terminally ill. Furthermore, such violent positions have lost, in the conscience of citizens, their criminal aspect, to the point where, by now, they are considered rights that the civil law must protect, while it is up to the state to guarantee their application by means of free organizations and services. The laws against life have not been promulgated by tyrants, nor by totalitarian regimes. On the contrary, these laws often benefit from the consensus of a sizable part of the citizens, who evidently do not realize how unjust these laws are. Keeping this problem in mind, but also many other violent manifestations that afflict the world— merciless wars, terrorism, bloody ethnic conflicts, drugs, exploitation, etc.–*Evangelium vitae* concludes that "The twentieth century will have been an era of massive attacks on life, an endless series of wars and a continual taking of innocent human life" (*EV*, 17).

If *Donum vitae* is concerned with problems arising from biotechnology, *Evangelium vitae* is preoccupied with the impending

172

threat of a paradigm—an inhumane and imbalanced war of those in power against the weak—that puts the survival of civilization itself at risk. For this reason, the encyclical transcends the typical doctrinal context of bioethical documents, to the point of acquiring the profundity and magnitude of ideas, characteristic of the great social encyclicals. By now, it is not a question of offering only ethical judgment on specific problems (customs, attitudes, laws, etc.), but, rather, of putting into action moral and spiritual resources that bring about an overturning of the situation, and a social and cultural recovery of the centrality of the human being and his or her innate dignity.

The encyclical also makes reference to a "conspiracy against life," in the sense that the present situation cannot be explained simplistically, but, instead, through the recognition of an entire series of elements that seem to have formed a common cause against life. Among these background factors, the pope cites: the obscuring of the positive value of human life, as a consequence of the scepticism prevalent in the contemporary mentality; certain *structures of sin* or conditions that make life choices burdensome and difficult; the overturning of certain traditional values, such as, for example, turning the poverty-stricken individual into a threatening subject from which it is necessary to defend oneself, and, therefore it is necessary to eliminate that individual; a concept of individuality counter-positioned against the community and the excercise of freedom apart from truth, etc.; but above all, what the pope calls the "heart of the tragedy being experienced by modern man: *the eclipse of the meaning of God and of man,* typical of a social and cultural climate dominated by secularism" (*EV*, 21). Consequently,

> The moral conscience, both individual and social, is today subjected, also as a result of the penetrating influence of the media, to an *extremely serious and mortal danger:* that of *confusion between good and evil,* precisely in relation to the fundamental right to life. (*EV*, 24)

At this point, having proposed the root cause of the phenomenon of threats against humanity in terms of eclipses, obscurity, and confusion, etc., the encyclical proposes to recover and proclaim the value of human life. This is the essential aspect of the document, which is originally featured in the title of the encyclical and makes it unique. The *gospel of life* consists of two parts. The first is derived from the explanation of the fifth commandment; the second proclaims Christ's calling of man to true life.

The Value of Life in Light of the Fifth Commandment

The prohibition in the commandment—*Do not kill*—has been, in all populations and cultures, the principal moral defense against individual and collective acts of violence. Therefore, it does not seem unjustified to suppose that the current diffusion of aggressive behavior can correspond to a weakening in the perception of this prohibition, which, moreover, belongs to the natural law; that is, it is profoundly rooted in the rational nature of persons.

The part of the encyclical that is more doctrinally focused is precisely chapter 3, dedicated to a detailed exposition of the content, biblical foundation, and rational justification of the commandment "Do not kill." The whole text is clearly organized to reaffirm through the solemn definition of three ethical principles the value of life and its inviolability. The first, of a more general nature, declares that "*the direct and voluntary killing of an innocent human being is always gravely immoral*" (*EV*, 57). The other two apply this norm to two types of behavior that constitute the most serious infraction of the beginning and end of life, asserting that "*direct abortion, that is, abortion willed as an end or as a means, always constitutes a grave moral disorder*" (*EV*, 62), and that, equally, "*euthanasia is a grave violation of the law of God*" (*EV*, 65).

It seems evident that the chapter takes into account the debate on the absolute value of natural moral law which has dominated moral theology in these latest years. According to the thesis sustained by some moralists, one cannot really talk of norms of absolute value, because these either have an indeterminate nature (and, in this case, would only serve as indicators of human goodness without imposing precise moral obligations), or they have a determinate formulation and would then be valid only in some concrete situations. In other words, the norms of the natural law would not be valid *semper et pro semper*—that is, for all people, in every case and circumstance—but only *ut in pluribus*, that is, in the majority of cases. This means recognizing the existence of exceptions, more or less consistent, according to the concrete precept that one is discussing.[2] In order to illustrate a thesis of this

---

[2] The question has already been confronted in the encyclical *Veritatis splendor*, which has qualified such a thesis as incompatible with the Catholic moral tradition.

kind, the fifth commandment has been cited frequently. The expression "Do not kill" would represent, above all, an affirmation of the fact that life is ordinarily a gift to a person, without excluding, however, the contrary, at least in some limited situations. In any case, this kind of expression should not be taken as an absolute rule, because there are circumstances in which it would be legitimate to kill. According to this thesis, legitimate defense, the death penalty, and just war would represent exceptions to the norm that prohibits homicide.

The problem is certainly complex, and the encyclical does not confront it with theoretical terms, because another encyclical, *Veritatis splendor*, has recently dealt with this argument. Instead, *Evangelium vitae*, presenting with great authority the three principles cited above, wants to confirm three determinate moral norms, which, on the one hand, prove evident in their precise moral content—in fact, they don't need further explanations—and on the other hand, they are always and in all circumstances confirmed as valid. The cited principles are none other than concrete determinations, obvious within themselves, of the fifth precept of the Decalogue. All three express absolute prohibitions which do not allow for exceptions: no reason, however serious or dramatic as it may appear, can justify the killing of an innocent man or woman.[3] The same judgment applies to the initial and final moments of human existence, which are those in most danger, as has already been mentioned before.

It has been said that the principal aim of *Evangelium vitae* is to propose pastoral instructions, to be confirmed with particular insistence, in order to oppose the influences of a culture of death. Or else, that *Evangelium vitae* does not presume to do anything other than to explain, with a language particularly in keeping with the nature of the Church, the features that must inspire the action of Christians in contemporary society. Yet, independently of the obvious reasons of opportunity, it deals with principles that go beyond the signs of the times and that must be received as immutable truths that form an esential part of the Christian message on life. The encyclical eliminates any perplexity about the intentions of the Holy Father to propose three definitive and irreformable principles, whose certainty is guaranteed by the

---

[3] *EV*, 55. The defense of life authorizes, in an extreme case where no other alternative remains, bringing about the death of an unjust aggressor. Even in this case, however, the intention should not be the death of another person, but rather the protection of a life in danger. Hatred—wanting to harm someone—is never permissible.

personal appeal of infallibility that corresponds to the ordinary Magisterium of the Church, a direct expression of the *munus docendi* that Christ granted to Peter and the other apostles and to their legitimate successors.

One arrives at such a conclusion by either examining the history of the papal document, or by considering the language and context with which the three cited principles are proposed.

With regard to the history, John Paul II himself recalls the principle stages: the convening, in the first days of the month of April in 1991, of an exceptional consistory with the participation of 112 cardinals from all over the world. The work of the cardinals was concluded with the pope's request for a solemn reaffirmation "of the constant teaching of the Church on the value and inviolability of human life, in light of current circumstances and of the attempts which threaten it today."[4]

In order to meet the request of the cardinals, which the Holy Father immediately wished to accommodate, there were fundamentally two possibilities: either to propose a definition *ex cathedra* (special Magisterium), or else, to render explicitly and unequivocally the consensus of all the bishops in the teaching of a concrete moral principle (ordinary Magisterium).

The first solution did not present particular difficulties, also keeping in mind the debate over these past few decades, and, above all, after the publication of Paul VI's encyclical *Humanae vitae*, on the opportunity of an *ex cathedra* definition in a moral matter. Cardinal Ratzinger dispelled any uncertainty in this regard, recalling, in the opening conference of the consistory, the doctrinal validity of the principle "the direct killing of an innocent human being is always a grave matter."[5]

The second solution found a solid precedent in the declaration of Vatican Council II (which takes up a principle established a century ago by the previous Vatican Council)[6] according to which the bishops

> proclaim infallibly the doctrine of Christ on the following conditions: namely, when, even though dispersed throughout the world but preserving for all that amongst

[4] *L'Osservatore Romano*, April 8-9, 1991.

[5] *L'Osservatore Romano*, April 5, 1991. In 1987 the American moralist G. Grisez published an interesting work with the title "The Definition of the Proposition: 'The Intentional Killing of an Innocent Human Being Is Always Grave Matter,'" in *Aa. Vv., Persona, Verità e Morale* (Rome: Città Nuova, 1987), 291-314.

[6] First Vatican Ecumenical Council, Dogmatic Constitution *Dei Filius*, 3.

themselves and with Peter's successor the bond of communion, in their authoritative teaching concerning matters of faith and morals, they are in agreement that a particular teaching is to be held definitively and absolutely. (*Lumen gentium*, 25)

The pope can teach a doctrine in an infallible way through an extraordinary and solemn act, just as with a dogmatic declaration. Yet, with the same amount of authority he can propose a sentence to be held immutable unanimously by all the bishops of the Church in communion with the Successor of Peter. The problem, more than anything, is how to make visible the unanimity of the College of Bishops.

John Paul II chose the second solution. Two months after the consistory he sent a letter to all of the bishops urging their collaboration. In this way he opened a dialogue that had to make clear the convergence of more than four thousand bishops dispersed all over the world. Actually, the response of the prelates was clear, as the encyclical itself underlines, "their unanimous desire to share in the doctrinal and pastoral mission of the Church with regard to the *Gospel of life*" (*EV*, 5).

The language and the syntax used in the formulation of the three principles unfailingly confirm what we have pointed out: on the one hand, the technical precision of the terms used; on the other hand, the infrequent emphatic style[7] which underlines that "solemnity" that was urged by the cardinals. But, above all they are the words that precede and accompany each of the three declarations,[8] to give its measure of theological value. They follow

[7] John Paul II used this formula last year in a letter in which he confirmed that the priesthood is reserved for men (see *De ordinatione sacerdotale*, May 22, 1994).

[8] Here are the words used. Regarding the inviolability of the innocent: "by the authority which Christ conferred upon Peter and his Successors, and in communion with the Bishops of the Catholic Church, *I confirm that the direct and voluntary killing of an innocent human being is always gravely immoral.* This doctrine, based upon that unwritten law which man, in the light of reason, finds in his own heart (cf. *Rom* 1:14-15), is reaffirmed by Sacred Scripture, transmitted by the Tradition of the Church and taught by the ordinary and universal Magisterium" (*EV*, 57).

Regarding abortion: "by the authority which Christ conferred upon Peter and his Successors, in comunion with the Bishops—who on various occasions have condemned abortion and who in the aforementioned consultation, albeit dispersed throughout the world, have shown unanimous agreement concerning this doctrine—*I declare that direct abortion, that is, abortion willed as an end or as a means, always constitutes a grave moral disorder,* since it is the deliberate killing of an innocent human being. This doctrine is based upon the natural law and upon the written Word of God, is transmitted by the Church's Tradition and taught by the ordinary and universal Magisterium" (*EV*, 62).

Regarding euthanasia: "in harmony with the Magisterium of my Predecessors and in communion with the Bishops of the Catholic Church, *I confirm that euthanasia is a grave violation of the law of God,* since it is the deliberate and morally unacceptable killing of a

a very precise plan: the invocation of one's supreme teaching authority as Successor of Peter, declaration of communion with the College of Bishops, statement of principle, and finally, indication of doctrinal sources: the natural law, the written Word of God, the living Church tradition, and its enduring universal and ordinary Magisterium. It is obvious that it does not want to leave any doubt on the infallibility of the proposed teaching.

Evangelium vitae wants to dispel doubtful attitudes,[9] strengthen the certainties of believers and of all those in whom the culture of death may have weakened the conviction of the absolute inviolability of innocent human life. It points towards overcoming an uncertain moral sensitivity and towards redeeming the role of conscience in making free and autonomous decisions, in accordance with the dignity of the human being, contrary to ethical relativism, understood as the utopian pretense of affirming freedom, while releasing it from any form of truth.

The encyclical warns about the danger of "fundamentalism," recognizing that in history there is no lack of crimes that have been committed in the name of a "truth," manipulated according to one-sided interests. But it clearly warns, just as much, that history is witness to other crimes no less serious, significantly tied to radical negations of freedom, that have been committed, and still continue to be committed today, when moral truth is rejected. Where there is no norm that binds the freedom of all, the risk is more than ever imminent to the weak, who remain at the mercy of the strong. A system that is stable and of just security for all, without discrimination, is only possible on the basis of recognizing

> those essential and innate human and moral values which flow from the very truth of the human being and express and safeguard the dignity of the person: values which no individual, no majority and no State can ever create, modify or destroy. (*EV*, 71)

Among these values one finds precisely the inviolability and the sacredness of innocent human life, including either that of an unborn child, or that of the ill or the elderly in the final stages of their existence.

human person. This doctrine is based upon the natural law and upon the written Word of God, is transmitted by the Church's Tradition and taught by the ordinary and universal Magisterium" (*EV*, 65).

[9] For example, in the already-cited document on priestly ordination, John Paul II explains *expressis verbis* that it was his intention in writing the letter *ut omne dubium auferatur* (to eliminate once and for all any type of doubt).

The Vocation to Life

It would be an error to conclude, from what has been said up until now, that the principal justification of the new encyclical of John Paul II should be looked for in the three cited principles. At least, I personally do not agree with this opinion. When one presumes to recover or develop major moral sensitivity with regard to human life, it is necessary to remember those limits that must be respected by everyone. This, however, is only the premise, or the part that we can consider as "defensive." However, if the problem really consists in a weakening of the perception of the value of life, simply to remember a series of prohibitions that defend integrity will not necessarily add something more desirable or alluring to life. We respect many things that we do not like. In fact, this actually constitutes a not-so-small difficulty in understanding the reasons that require a respectful attitude when we are faced with things that seem unpleasant to us.

The fifth commandment, prohibiting homicide and suicide, indicates an ethical barrier that no one can cross. At first sight, however, it does not say much about the problem of the worth of living and allowing to live, and why. The precept "Do not kill" explains the will of God. From this, however, it does not follow that one cannnot desire to die, or cannot ask oneself if sometimes death may be a preferable alternative to life. Man needs something more than a prohibition. A veto tells him that something is illicit and, therefore, bad. However, when certain undoubtedly criminal behaviors (one thinks of perinatal euthanasia, of the experimentation upon human embryos, etc.) are justified with pretentious arguments, which eliminate either the dignity of the victims or their right to defend themselves and to be defended, it is clear that we are facing something much more serious than a "deprecative" violation of the Decalogue. Only a very serious pathology of conscience could present such injustices as minor wrongs, ethically useful or preferable. With such disturbed logic, it takes very little to end up judging these injustices as honest and honorable, and finally, to conclude that they are obligatory.

In *Familiaris consortio* (November 22, 1981), John Paul II calls this phenomenon the "anti-life mentality" (30). *Evangelium vitae* takes up again the reflections started there and brings them to their extreme consequences, especially in chapter 2, which explains the

Christian message on life. In my opinion, one finds here the principal novelty of the encyclical. The pope deliberately puts aside philosophical, scientific, and technological considerations that are in favor of life (to which he justly gave notable emphasis in other documents), in order to respond, almost exclusively on the basis of Christian doctrine, to questions such as: Is not life in some cases an intolerable burden? Is it worth living always and no matter what? Is the life of man really precious in every moment of its earthly existence?

John Paul II recognizes the multiplicity of situations, of experiences and of personal stories, even those that are most bitter and painful. But, it is precisely for this reason that he invites us to rediscover the preciousness of human existence in all of its magnificence, in light of what God has wanted to reveal. Human life seems fragile and contingent, exposed to thousands of dangers and deceptions. If it had not been present in the sacred texts as a precious gift in the eyes of the Creator and Redeemer of mankind, the life of man would propose an indecipherable enigma. Yet, the Christian announces the incredible event that the human creature is "*the object of God's gentle and intense love*" (*EV*, 31), that "*the life* which God offers to man *is a gift by which God shares something of himself with his creature*" (*EV*, 34), and that the human creature is called to reach his fulfillment in the life promised by Christ, which "*consists in being begotten of God and sharing the fulness of his love*" (*EV*, 37), etc.

They are strong affirmations, which echo the theological concept of the human person as a divine image. Affirmations that require an attentive and reflective reading of an encyclical, written at the opening of a new millenium, with the hope of being the spark for an epochal transformation of humanity.

CHAPTER 13

Change and Stability
in Morals

THE REVEREND BRIAN MULLADY, O.P.

The Terms of the Problem

In a recent article, "Development in Moral Doctrine," John T. Noonan makes the statement, "That the moral teachings of the Catholic Church have changed over time will, I suppose, be denied by almost no one today."[1] Noonan then goes on to examine the various teachings he thinks have changed over time. They are: usury, indissolubility of marriage, slavery, and religious freedom. In his recent encyclical on morals, *Veritatis splendor*, Pope John Paul II makes the statement:

> Consequently, respect for norms which prohibit such acts and oblige *semper et pro semper,* that is, without any exception, not only does not inhibit a good intention, but actually represents its basic expression.[2]

[1] John T. Noonan, Jr., "Development in Moral Doctrine," *Theological Studies* 54 (1993), 662-677.

[2] John Paul II, *Veritatis splendor* (August 6, 1993), section 82.

Semper et pro semper (literally, "always and forever") is a very final expression. The pope is underlining the fact that there are certain moral acts that never can change in their moral evaluation.

Can these two positions be reconciled with each other? If not, how can one explain the facts Noonan brings out in his well-documented article? Though it is true that Catholicism has maintained that there can be change in all doctrines, this change was always looked on as a homogeneous evolution of deeper understanding of the mind of the apostles themselves. Noonan argues in all the above-mentioned cases that

> In the course of this displacement of one set of principles, what was forbidden became lawful (the cases of usury and marriage); what was permissible became unlawful (the case of slavery); and what was required became forbidden (the persecution of heretics).[3]

Noonan goes on to say that he has found "no great theologians [who] have immersed themselves deeply in these mutations of morals." He reasons that there are three basic types of response on the part of theologians to the facts of change. There are those who claim there is no change; those who see the real development as making the implicit more explicit and those who see development of doctrine as a perfection not a distortion of a previous tradition. Another response was that of the Modernists, whom he admits fell into the trap of making doctrine merely a projection of human need. The first type of response is merely "an apologetic tactic incapable of execution and unworthy of belief." The second is "incredible: [for] the acceptance of slavery did not imply freedom, the endorsement of religious persecution did not entail respect for religious freedom." The third position, which is that of Cardinal Newman has some merit. He says that it "is adaptable to the development of moral doctrine." Yet, he does not develop this point any further. He then finds the Modernist position wanting because the "position that human needs will shape doctrine carries the cost of eliminating any objective content."[4]

He now gives his own solution, which is a fifth position. According to him, this is the position of Vatican II, which he also identifies as that of Jesus Christ. To explain this position he quotes Bernard Häring and his commentary on Vatican II.

---

[3] Noonan, "Development," 669.

[4] Ibid., the five quotations in this paragraph appear on 669, 671, 671, 672, and 672.

Christ does not become greater through ongoing history, but our knowledge of the plan of salvation which is revealed in the world in Christ does become more complete and close to life in our hearts through the working of the Spirit in the history of the Church and above all in the saints.[5]

This is very true, but the question must now be asked as to the catalyst and content of the newer insight. For Noonan, this explanation must be sought in the changing social structures of the Western world and perhaps other worlds as well. Cultural confrontation is what leads the Church to change moral teaching. Here he summarizes the work of the moralist Louis Vereecke: "Moral theology is where the unchanged gospel encounters changing cultures."[6]

One could conclude that the Church demands the cultural input of secular society in order to discover the true meaning of the gospel. "The gospel as interpreted by Protestants and as mediated by Rousseau and the revolutionaries of 1789, achieved much." The changing times and climates of cultures led the Church to discover what was truly contained in the commands of Christ and the Old and New Law. After examining various shifts in culture as to marriage, usury, slavery, and religious freedom, he concludes, "All these factors, plus re-evaluation of the words of Christ, created the new moral doctrine."[7]

One could further conclude that the nature of the gospel can never be discovered by the Church in any definitive way about anything. Ultimately, "All will be judged by the demands of the day in which they live." Attempts to seek unchanging moral norms would be vain then. All moral teachings are substantially evolving. "Must not the traditional motto *semper idem* be modified, however unsettling that might be, in the direction of *plus ça change, plus c'est la même chose?*"[8]

Noonan then applies this explanation to certain historical facts. The historical climate has been the occasion that has led the Church to emphasize different aspects of the gospel. But does the Church really need the interlinear version of the Gospel supplied by Rousseau and the Enlightenment to interpret gospel values

---

[5] Bernard Häring, *My Witness for the Church*, trans. Leonard Swidler (New York: Paulist, 1992), 122, as quoted in Noonan, "Development," 672.

[6] Noonan ("Development," 673) cites Louis Vereecke, *Storia della teologia morale moderna* (Rome: Lateran, 1979), 1.4-5.

[7] Both quotations are from Noonan, "Development," 675 and 676.

[8] Ibid., 676 and 677.

correctly? Noonan wants to support unchanging values. Yet, the thesis that the morality of the Gospels can only be substantially changed by subtraction so that what was wrong is now right and what was right is now wrong in the light of the changing expressions of culture and history seems to undercut that thesis. Did the Church really have to experience the Enlightenment thinkers to know that slavery was immoral? Was not the gospel sufficiently clear on this subject already?

One can even go a step further and ask if the moral teachings of the gospel are just vague general principles which change and develop according to the culture of each age. If so, then it is difficult to see how one can maintain there are any absolute, specific moral norms. One must also maintain that the Church should adapt itself to the culture to discover what the true teaching of Christ is. These are grave questions and the solutions to them are not simple.

One can summarize the points and issues raised by Noonan's article thus:

1. One must attend to history and the experience of culture in order to have an ongoing application of the gospel that is correct and conforms to the mind of Christ.
2. History demonstrates beyond a doubt that there is no definable, specific, unchanging law behind Catholic moral teaching, but a continuous attempt to approximate what Christ commanded of us in at least four areas— slavery, the indissolubility of marriage, usury, and religious freedom. These approximations can actually be denials of previous teaching.
3. The Magisterium should then attend to each culture and its moral values to find a standard on the basis of which the Church must interpret the moral teaching of the gospel in each age.
4. Therefore, every traditional moral teaching of the Church should be continuously examined in light of the spirit of the age to see if it is sound.

Many modern moralists would find themselves in agreement with these propositions.[9] They must be realistically put to the test to see if they are true. The long and short of the question can be reduced to three questions. Is there an unchanging law at

[9] See, for example, the host of modern moralists treated in Théo G. Belmans, "*L'immutabilité de la loi naturelle selon saint Thomas d'Aquin,*" *Revue Thomiste*, 87, n. 1 (1987), 23-44.

the basis of Catholic moral teaching? If so, how can one explain the fact of historical change that is occasionally observed in Catholic moral teaching? Are the historical examples of a shift in the moral teaching of the Church truly the Church listening to culture and modifying belief or are they merely occasions when the Church emphasized another aspect of the gospel? In Scholastic language, are they material or formal changes?

The Source of Catholic Moral Norms

Exceptionless moral norms have traditionally been based in the natural law. This is human reason examining those actions that befit human nature. If moral norms must be subject to their cultural context to be true, this implies that human nature must be modified according to the spirit of the age. The natural law must therefore change formally in each culture and in each age.

The problem of the changing natural law must be rooted in the problem of a changing nature. If the nature of man is fluid, then all expressions of law in human actions would be indifferent morally and would need to be constantly modified according to historical experience. The natural law would merely be a kind of occasionalism. The first point to establish is that the natural law is right reason which truly expresses the actions that befit human nature. This does not mean it is fatalistic or physicalist. Nature here is not the fixed laws of inalterable reason of the Enlightenment. Still, the basic content of the natural law must be based on the interrelation of the powers of the soul which are themselves inalterable. Freedom presupposes them, it does not continuously modify them. "This law is called 'natural,' not in reference to the nature of irrational beings, but because reason which decrees it properly belongs to human nature."[10]

When man gives expression from his own reason to the kinds of actions that fulfill his nature and the kinds of action that must be avoided because they preclude the fulfillment of his nature, then he may be said to be expressing the natural law. Human reason must evaluate material things and emotions in addition to spiritual things because man is by nature a composite of body and soul. "The spiritual and immortal soul is the principle of unity of the human being, whereby it exists as a whole—*corpore et anima unus*—as a person.... *The person, including the body, is completely*

[10] *Catechism of the Catholic Church*, English translation (Mahwah, N.J.: Paulist Press, 1994), no. 1955.

185

entrusted to himself, and it is in the unity of body and soul that the person is the subject of his own moral acts."[11]

If the natural law is not a true expression of the perfection of human being, then there would be no objective standard by which men could judge their conduct apart from themselves or their social, historical, and cultural situation. The truth about man must include the truth about human nature. "The subject is the sole author of the judgement, but he is not the author of its truth."[12] The author of the truth about nature is God to whom the subject must conform his judgment. *"Nature cannot be conquered by violating its laws."*[13] Rather, the freedom of the person is realized precisely by respecting who he is, which includes the objective relation of his soul and body. "Justice towards the Creator, on the part of man, comprises…two elements: obedience to the order of nature and emphasis on the value of the person."[14]

True, the objective nature which is the basis for the subjective judgment can seem to be very different depending on the place, time, and even the person. The new *Catechism of the Catholic Church* states the point succinctly:

> Application of the natural law varies greatly; it can demand reflection that takes account of various conditions of life according to place, times, and circumstances. Nevertheless, in the diversity of cultures, the natural law remains as a rule that binds men among themselves and imposes on them, beyond the inevitable differences, common principles.
>
> The natural law is *immutable* and permanent throughout the variations of history (cf. *Gaudium et spes* 10); it subsists under the flux of ideas and customs and supports their progress. The rules that express it remain substantially valid. Even when it is rejected in its very principles, it cannot be destroyed or removed from the heart of man. It always arises again in the life of individuals and societies.[15]

Though this text states that the natural law remains "substantially valid," does not the fact that this law is variously applied contradict this? Does this not suggest that human nature is changeable? In fact, even St. Thomas Aquinas, who holds for the

[11] John Paul II, *Veritatis splendor*, 48.
[12] Karol Wojtyla, *Love and Responsibility* (London: Collins, 1981), note 43, p. 302.
[13] Ibid., 229.
[14] Ibid., 247.
[15] *Catechism*, 1957 and 1958.

substantial validity of the principles of the natural law, says that human nature is changeable.[16] St. Thomas further remarks in the same text that the just and the good must often be determined by "diverse conditions of man and things, according to the diversity of places and time."[17] Does this not mean that culture, and not the powers common to every man, formally determines human nature?

Just how can human nature be considered changeable? St. Thomas indicates that human nature can be considered in two ways: from the standpoint of the species which is universal and from the standpoint of the individual. "Something is said to be natural to each man in two ways: in one way, from the nature of the species; in another way from the nature of the individual."[18] What forms the difference between species and individual in man? It is the difference between the relationship of the human body as the necessary instrument of the soul common to all men and the individual relationship of each soul to that individual body's unique physical composition which is special to each person.[19]

One could say that all men have the same powers of soul which demand the same integrity and the same virtues. Yet some virtues are formed in those powers of the soul that are reducible to the human species as such, like justice.

Other virtues are formed in those powers of the soul that are reducible to powers that respect also the different physical constitution of each man, and so have to do with the passions which vary greatly from one individual to the next, like fortitude and temperance. Each man must deal with fear, but because the body of each is uniquely formed materially, some must become courageous despite great tendency to fear, others must become courageous by not foolishly disregarding fear.

Regarding the passions, then, human nature would be changeable, not as to the common relationship of body to soul, but as to how each individual emotional constitution approached the mean in fortitude and temperance. There would thus be a

---

[16] "*Et hoc contingit propter mutabilitatem naturae humanae*" (Thomas Aquinas, *De malo*, 2, 4, *ad* 13). (Translations of Aquinas' Latin, unless otherwise noted, are my own.)

[17] "...[*E*]*t diversas conditiones hominum et rerum, secundum diversitatem locorum et temporum...*" (ibid.).

[18] "...[*A*]*liquid dicitur alicui homini naturale dupliciter: uno modo, ex natura speciei; alio modo, ex natura individui*" (Thomas Aquinas, *Summa theologiae*, I-II, 63, 1, *corp.*; hereafter this work will be cited as *ST*).

[19] "*Si autem consideremus naturam hominis ex parte speciei, scilicet, inquantum est rationalis...Si vero consideretur natura huius individui secundum propriam complexionem...*" (ibid., 46, 5, *corp.*).

subjective element in the natural law for these virtues, i.e., the individual temperament of each man. Universal reason must include the individual body of each man when the passions are concerned:

> But from the part of the body, according to the nature of the individual, there are some habits of desire according to natural beginnings. For there are some disposed from their own bodily complexion to chastity or meekness or things of this sort.[20]

It is this subjective factor that St. Thomas spoke about when he said that human nature was changeable.[21] This is not in species man nor the common elements of the species. What differs is the disposition of the passions because of the different dispositions of the body. This is not a change in general norms, but only in the manner a given individual approaches the norm because of bodily constitution.

In the virtue of justice, then, the mean is determined merely by objective standards with no subjective element as a part of their mean. What matters in justice is the just thing, not how the just man feels about it. This is because justice is found only in the will. Does this make justice absolutely the same everywhere? Yes, but one must distinguish. The just thing is formally the same, because it is what is due to another. But depending on the things being considered, the just standard may be materially different. This is not because the soul differs, or the persons exchanging the goods differ, but because circumstances may express this relationship in different ways depending on the social conditions. This is especially true in the exchange of material goods. This is another changeability in human nature and is the change in the natural law to which St. Thomas refers when he speaks of the variation in nature according to different times and places cited already.[22]

One could therefore generally sum up the changeability of human nature and thus the changeability of the natural law by saying that justice and goodness are always the same in species and form, though they may differ in the individual according to the material conditions. Those material conditions may either be

---

[20] "*Sed ex parte corporis, secundum naturam individui, sunt aliqui habitus appetitivi secundum inchoationes naturales. Sunt enim quidam dispositi ex propria corporis complexione ad castitatem vel mansuetudinem, vel ad aliquid huiusmodi*" (ibid., 51, 1, *corp.*).

[21] See footnote 16 above.

[22] See footnote 17 above.

within the person himself because of his bodily constitution, as in the case of virtues that respect the passions, or outside the person in the temporal circumstances of time and place, as in the case of the exchange of goods in justice. One can now place the reference in St. Thomas to the changeability of human nature in its complete context.

> Just and good acts may be considered in two ways: in one way formally, and thus they are always and everywhere the same, because the principles of law, which are in natural reason do not change; in another way, materially, and thus the just and the good are not the same everywhere and for all men, but must be determined by law. This happens because of the changeability of human nature and the diverse conditions of men and things, according to diverse times and places.[23]

One can therefore see that human law may take into account various material differences or the needs caused by various occasions in history in the application of the natural law. This application is merely a practical addition to the norm.[24] These practical additions do not change the natural law by making what was evil good or what was good evil. This would be to change the natural law by subtraction. In fact, the natural law can only be changed by way of addition according to what suits human needs at the time. This change may be done by divine law as when God commands something by way of dispensation from the natural law, or *by human law*.[25]

These additions are necessary either materially or occasionally to preserve the fundamental character of the goods of the human soul. These additions would either promote the basic human good of the powers of the soul or tolerate certain social evils

---

[23] "*Justa et bona possunt dupliciter considerari: uno modo formaliter, et sic semper et ubique sunt eadem; quia principia iuris quae sunt in naturali ratione non mutantur. Alio modo materialiter, et sic non sunt eadem justa et bona ubique et apud omnes, sed oportet ea lege determinari. Et hoc contingit proter mutabilitatem naturae humanae et diversas conditiones hominum et rerum, secundum diversitatem locorum et temporum*" (Aquinas, *De malo*, 2, 4, ad 13).

[24] "*...[L]ex naturalis potest intelligi mutari dupliciter. Uno modo, per hoc quod aliquid ei addatur. Et sic nihil prohibet legem naturalem mutari: multa enim supra legem naturalem superaddita sunt, ad humanam vitam utilia, tam per legem divinam, quam etiam per leges humanas*" (*ST*, I-II, 94, 5, corp.).

[25] "*Ad tertium dicendum quod aliquid dicitur esse de iure naturali dupliciter. Uno modo, quia ad hoc natura inclinat, sicut non esse iniuriam alteri faciendum. Alio modo, quia natura non induxit contrarium, sicut possemus dicere quod hominem esse nudum est de iure naturali, quia natura non dedit ei vestitum, sed ars invenit. Et hoc modo 'communis omnium possessio, et omnium una libertas,' dicitur esse de iure naturali, quia scilicet distinctio possessionum et servitus non sunt inductae a natura, sed per hominum rationem ad utilitatem humanae vitae*" (ibid., ad 3).

which in the occasion would be necessary to preserve the general social good of society required for the pursuit of good of the soul. These additions could never recommend these evils without making the basis of society unjust and contrary to nature.

Many of these additions fall under what the Catholic tradition has termed the "right of nations." This right is not exactly natural law. This right is the common determination of the majority of reasonable people about the best way circumstantially to preserve the values contained in the natural law. This right can be expressed in positive law. As the "right of nations" is an approximation based on human prudence, it can change sometimes with changing social conditions. One modern, free translation of the *Summa theologiae* puts it thus:

> Things can be by nature right either because nature inclines us towards them (e.g. not doing harm to others), or because nature does not incline us to the contrary (going naked, since clothes are products of artifice not of nature). *Common ownership and universal freedom are by nature right* in this latter sense, because private property and slavery are not arrangements of nature but human contrivances for the good running of society.[26]

What sort of changes are the changes in Catholic moral teaching about usury, indissolubility of marriage, slavery, and religious freedom that Professor Noonan enumerates? Are they formal changes, material changes, or merely occasional changes that involve the application of the natural law to human law?

Money and Marriage

Let us take first the two places where Professor Noonan maintains Catholic doctrine has completely changed which are more easily treated: problems concerning money and marriage. Professor Noonan himself admits that the changes these doctrines have undergone are not perhaps as sweeping as they seem at first glance. He states about usury, the place where he perceives one very drastic change that, "The change can be exaggerated."[27] Following the principles enumerated above, one must ask how money fulfills the powers of the human soul. Has the change in

---

[26] Thomas Aquinas, *Summa Theologiae: A Concise Translation*, ed. Timothy McDermott (Westminster, Md.: Christian Classics, 1992), 288; the Latin version of this text (*ST*, I-II, 94, 5, *ad* 3) is reproduced in the preceding note.

[27] Noonan, "Development," 662.

Church teaching been of the species, the individual, or the occasion?

Money serves the needs of the body, which serves the needs of the soul. Money always has a human dimension then. Pope John Paul II has expressed this well in *Laborem exercens*.[28] One can never make money a commodity that simply obeys the laws of supply and demand or a thing that surpasses human value. The capitalist notion that money or commerce are ends in themselves which obey their own intrinsic laws is still condemned as contrary to both the natural law and the gospel by the Church.[29] Money, like all material goods, cannot be an end in itself. Moreover, money must express the relation of justice between individuals who exchange it.

This idea of money has always been at the root of the theory of capital in the Church. Even as early as St. Thomas, interest on a loan is defined in two ways. In his *De malo*, St. Thomas affirms the traditional distinction that is found in Aristotle about interest on goods consumed in use and goods not consumed in use. Goods consumed in use cannot be justly redeemed by more than was given. Such would be the case if one charged interest on a loan of money that was consumed in use for the sake of survival, for example.

In an objection, however, he further distinguishes between money consumed in use and money used as a pledge to make more money. He looks upon the latter as a secondary use of money that is not consumed in use. For example, there would be a difference between food stamps consumed in use to buy necessary goods and a loan to purchase a house from which the purchaser would gain some equity himself. In the former case it would be unjust to charge interest; in the latter it would be just to charge moderate interest.

> And therefore if someone lends his own money to another
> for the use of exchange, which is the proper end of money,
> and for this use asks interest from the other above the money
> given, this will be contrary to justice; if however someone
> lends his own money to another for the use of the other in

---

[28] "*In all cases of this sort, in every social situation of this type, there is a confusion or even a reversal of the order laid down from the beginning by the words of the Book of Genesis: Man is treated as an instrument of production, whereas he—he alone, independent of the work he does—ought to be treated as the effective subject of work and its true maker and creator*" (John Paul II, *Laborem exercens* (September 14, 1981), 7).

[29] See John Paul II, *Centesimus annus* (May 1, 1991).

which the money is not consumed, the same argument will apply which occurs in things which are not consumed in use, which licitly are hired out and contracted for. So if someone lends a designated amount of money in a little sack to someone so that he might use it as a stake (capital investment) and then accepts interest this is not usury; because one does not find simple money lending there, but more hiring out and contracting of money.[30]

Clearly the latter use of money is very much in conformity with the idea of capital investment. In fact, money itself is used as the example of how formal principles may be applied differently by human law at different times and places in the text cited from *De malo*, 2, 4, *ad* 13.

...[F]or example, it is always just that an equivalent exchange be given in buying and selling, but it is just that at one time and place so much be given for a measure of grain, and at another place or time another amount which is greater or lesser.[31]

This is not a change in the natural law, but rather its material application based on occasion.

As to marriage, this objection is easily answered. The Pauline privilege is based on a text in St. Paul (1 Cor. 7:10-16). According to the *Code of Canon Law*, the Pauline privilege consists in this:

A marriage entered by two non-baptized persons is dissolved by means of the pauline privilege in favor of the faith of the party who has received baptism by the very fact that a new marriage is contracted by the party who has been baptized, provided the non-baptized party departs.[32]

Though it is true that general exegesis of the passage in St. Paul perhaps does not explicitly justify the later interpretation given to

---

[30] "*Et ideo si quis pecuniam suam alteri concedat ad usum commutationis, qui est proprius pecuniae, et pro hoc usu pretium aliud quaerat ultra sortem, erit contra iustitiam; si vero aliquis concedat alteri pecuniam suam ad usum alium quo pecunia non consumitur, erit eadem ratio quae est de rebus illis quae ipso usu non consumantur, quae licite locantur et conducuntur. Unde si quis pecuniam signatam in sacculo concedat alicui ad hoc quod ponat in pignore, et exinde pretium accipiat, non est usura; quia non est ibi contractus mutui, sed magis locatio et conductio*" (Thomas Aquinas, *De malo*, 13, 4, *ad* 15).

[31] "*...[S]icut hoc semper est iustum in emptione et venditione fiat commutatio secundum aequivalens; sed pro mensura frumenti iustum est ut in tali loco vel tempore tantum detur, et in alio loco vel tempore non tantum, sed plus vel minus*" (ibid., 2, 4, *ad* 13).

[32] *Code of Canon Law* (1983) c. 1143, sec. 1.

192

it by canon law, implicitly it certainly has been used since the fourth century to justify remarriage of a converted Catholic party when the non-baptized party cannot cohabit or when the baptized party wishes to enter into a sacramental marriage.

It is true that in the sixteenth century, this lack of cohabitation was extended to include those who could not cohabit after they had been converted, like slaves and captives in war or persecution. In fact, canon 1149 of the *Code of Canon Law* more or less expresses this application of Church law.[33] This was not a change in the moral theology of marriage but perhaps simply a broader interpretation of the certitude demanded to decide about the possibility of cohabitation. In other words, the Church's understanding of this dissolution of marriage has always been based on two points: the favor of baptism and thus sacramental marriage and the departure in some sense of the non-baptized party.[34]

Professor Noonan is correct when he says,

> Prior to 1924 the teaching of the Church expressly grounded on both the commandment of the Lord and on the natural law, was that marriage was indissoluble except in the special case of the conversion of an unbeliever.[35]

What I take him to mean here is that the marriage that was dissolved in all prior applications of the law was between two unbelievers. In the celebrated Helena, Montana case an unbaptized man married a baptized Protestant. He then divorced her. After this divorce, he converted to Catholicism. The Pope then dissolved this first marriage by virtue of his vicarious ministerial power. The only difference between this case and the cases before 1924 described by Professor Noonan is that the other party was baptized, whereas in all the others, the other parties were unbaptized. This hardly changes the fact of the non-sacramental marriage being dissolved in favor of baptism. It is in no sense a change in the theology of marriage, but merely a further

[33] "A non-baptized person who, once having received baptism in the Catholic Church, cannot restore cohabitation with a non-baptized spouse due to captivity or persecution can contract another marriage even if the other party received baptism in the meantime, with due regard for the prescription of can. 1141."

[34] See *The Code of Canon Law: A Text and Commentary*, ed. James A. Coriden, Thomas J. Green, and Donald E. Heintschel (New York: Paulist Press, 1985), 818-819; for example: "This type of dissolution differed from the Pauline privilege in that it involved direct action by the Supreme Pontiff, who dissolved such marriages in virtue of his vicarious ministerial power."

[35] Noonan, "Development," 664.

application of the principles to the canonical and ministerial power of the Church in the person of the pope.

Neither the change in the teaching on usury nor the change of the Pauline privilege can be looked upon as formal changes in the moral teaching of the Church. They are merely application to the individual of changing material situations. Those material situations may reflect the constant changing times and conditions of men, but they are not in any sense changes of principles based on the human soul and the law of God. They are rather clarifications of those powers.

Slavery

The question of slavery is a more difficult one. Professor Noonan cites several authorities who seem to maintain that slavery is not a sin. Then in the nineteenth century, he says the Church dramatically changed this teaching, until today the new *Catechism of the Catholic Church* lists slavery as an intrinsic evil. He summarizes: "In the light of the teachings of the modern popes and the Second Vatican Council on the dignity of the human person, it is morally unthinkable that one person be allowed to buy, sell, hypothecate, or lease another or dispose of that person's children."[36]

First, the authorities as to the good of slavery that Professor Noonan cites are generally local private theologians or Councils. There is also a much greater number of much more commonly recognized authorities who maintain that all slavery is contrary to the natural law.[37] Leo XIII quotes a number of these authorities to show that slavery is a natural evil in the encyclical he wrote on the abolition of slavery, *In plurimis*, promulgated on May 5, 1888.

He begins with Gregory the Great:

...[I]t is most fitting that men by the concession of manumission should restore to the freedom in which they were born those whom nature set free into the world, but who have been condemned to the yoke of slavery by the law of nations.[38]

Leo goes on to quote St. Augustine:

---

[36] Ibid., 666.
[37] See, for example, *New Catholic Encyclopedia*, s.v. "slavery."
[38] *Epist. lib.* 6, *ep.* 12 (*PL*77, 803C-804A); quoted in Leo XIII, *In plurimis*, 2.

Having created man a reasonable being, and after His own
likeness, God wished that he should rule over the brute
creation; that he should be the master, not of men, but of
beasts....[Therefore] the state of slavery is rightly regarded as
a penalty upon the sinner; thus, the word slave does not
occur in the Bible until the just man Noe branded with it the
sin of his son.   It was sin, therefore, which deserved this
name; *it was not natural.* (Emphasis added.)[39]

Pope Leo obviously sees the Catholic tradition as attributing
slavery to the condition of original sin and not to the original
nature of man as it sprung from the hand of God and it is on this
distinction that the solution to the problem rests. Many things are
introduced by human contrivance in the state of original sin which
were not according to the way God made the world. The term
"right or law of nations" expresses this human contrivance.

Slavery is assigned to that part of the natural law that is
termed the law of nations. Pope Leo quotes the Code of Justinian
as an example of the right of nations: "Slaves are in the power of
their masters, and this power is derived from the law of nations."[40]
The Pope says that though it was the common opinion in the pagan
world that people were naturally slaves, this has never
corresponded with the doctrine of Scripture or Tradition.

Whoever compare [*sic*] the pagan and the Christian attitude
toward slavery will easily come to the conclusion that the one
was marked by great cruelty and wickedness, and the other
by great gentleness and humanity, nor will it be possible to
deprive the Church of the credit due to her as the instrument
of this happy change.[41]

Pope Paul III applied this teaching during the settlement of
the New World which established the fact that both Indians and
Moorish slaves

all had a just and natural right of a threefold character,
namely, that each one of them was master of his own person,

[39] *Rationalem factum ad imaginem suam noluit nisi irrationabilibus dominari: non hominem homini, sed hominem pecori....Conditio servitutis iure intellegitur imposita peccatori. Proinde
nusquam Scripturarum legimus servum, antequam hoc vocabulo Noe iustus peccatum filii vindicaret*
(Gen. 9:25). *Nomen itaque istud culpa meruit, non natura."* Augustine, *De civitate Dei,* 19, 15
(*PL* 41, 643).

[40] Justinian, *"Insti.," lib.* I, *tit.* 8, *n.* 1; in *Corpus iuris civilis* (4th ed., Berlin, Weidmann,
1886) vol. 1, p. 3; quoted in Leo XIII, *In plurimis,* 16.

[41] Leo XIII, *In plurimis,* 9.

that they could live together under their own laws, and that they could acquire and hold property for themselves. More than this, having sent letters to the Cardinal Archbishop of Toledo, he pronounced an interdict and deprival of sacraments against those who acted contrary to the aforesaid decree, reserving to the Roman Pontiff the power of absolving them.[42]

Professor Noonan says this same Paul III praised "the benevolent effects of slavery on agriculture while approving the traffic in slaves in Rome." But surely, in light of the above quotation, Paul III must be interpreted as finding some reason for the toleration of slavery as an evil, not its approval. Professor Noonan expresses this very point in saying that one of the great, classic moralists Juan De Lugo "was in harmony with the moralists' tradition when he found slavery 'beyond the intention of nature,' but 'introduced to prevent greater evils.'"[43]

One should therefore conclude that Scripture, Tradition, and Magisterium have never taught that slavery was in accord with the natural law and therefore a good. St. Thomas may be permitted to state it.

> Now, the more dearly a thing is loved according to nature, the more perfect it is to despise it, for the sake of Christ. Nothing is dearer to any man than the freedom of his will, whereby he is lord of others, can use what he pleases, can enjoy what he wills, and is master of his own actions. . . . [Therefore] nothing is so repugnant to human nature as slavery.[44]

> For slavery is more abhorrent to our nature than is death.[45]

In these texts, St. Thomas seems to be expressing the same thought as Vatican II. Yet in other texts, St. Thomas seems to be expressing the same distinction found in De Lugo and the whole tradition referred to by Leo XIII that slavery is found in that part of the natural law called the "law of nations."

> A thing is said to belong to the natural law in two ways. First, because nature inclines thereto: e.g. that one should not do

[42] Paul III (1534-49), *Veritas ipsa*, (June 2, 1559); quoted in Leo XIII, In *plurimis*, 16.
[43] Noonan, "Development," 666.
[44] Thomas Aquinas, *De perfectione spiritualis vitae, c.* 10.
[45] Ibid., *c.* 14.

harm to another. Secondly, because nature did not bring in the contrary....In this sense, 'the possession of all things in common and universal freedom' are said to be of the natural law, because, to wit, the distinction of possessions and slavery were not brought in by nature, but devised by human law for the benefit of human life. Accordingly the law of nature was not changed in this respect except by addition.[46]

One can see that there is no contradiction between these two series of texts if one considers slavery in the context of the various states of human nature. St. Thomas affirms that absolutely speaking there can be no relationship between master and slave in the state of original innocence when man was created right. This relation only enters with the condition of original sin, an addition made by human law. The addition did not make slavery right. The sense of the addition can only be seen in light of the fallen nature of man.

Mastership has a twofold meaning. First, as opposed to slavery, in which sense a master means one to whom another is subject as a slave. In another sense mastership is referred in a general sense to any kind of subject; and in this sense even he who has the office of governing and directing free men, can be called a master. In the state of innocence man could have been a master of men, not in the former but in the latter sense.[47]

Further, slavery "is of the positive law; whereas marriage is of natural and Divine law."[48] So it would seem that slavery is not in the "first intention of nature."[49] It did not exist in the state of original justice because slavery makes one man simply an object of use[50] and no man can ever be an object of use. Why was it permitted then?

The human reasoning that produced slavery is similar to the human reasoning of Moses that permitted divorce in the state of original sin. Christ is asked the question in the Scriptures about Moses permitting divorce (Mt. 19:8). Christ says that Moses permitted divorce because of the "hardness of heart" of the men living in the state of original sin. This "hardness of heart" would

[46] Thomas Aquinas, *ST*, I-II, 94, 5, *ad* 3.
[47] Ibid., I, 96, 4, *corp.*
[48] Ibid., *Suppl.*, 52, 2, *corp.*
[49] Ibid., 1, *ad* 2.
[50] "*Ad propriam utilitatem sui*," ibid., I, 96, 4, *corp.*

refer to what theologians have traditionally called the concupiscence or weakness that results from the original sin. One opinion about this permission was that Moses allowed it because he knew that the men would try to free themselves from the marriage obligation by killing their innocent wives if they were not allowed to divorce them. This did not make divorce any the less a sin against the marriage covenant. Moses permitted divorce not because he approved of it, but because in the actual situation it was the only way to protect the innocent lives of the wives. So, this permission was granted only in light of the protection of the innocent in the situation of lust resulting from original sin.

The original unity of man and woman was one without lust and shame. This became compromised when man lost grace in the original sin. The lust that entered marriage as a result of the loss of grace tended to emphasize only the right of procreation to the expense of the unitive dimension. Wives came to be looked on only as property useful for procreation, not as persons in their own right. The precepts of the Old Testament reflected this legalistic and casuistic interpretation. In the text on Moses permitting a decree of divorce, Christ does not accept the attempt to reduce marriage to human reasoning and refers to "the beginning" or to the state of nature before the original sin.

> Therefore adultery was opposed only within special limits and within the sphere of definitive premises which make up the essential form of the Old Testament ethos. Adultery is understood above all (and maybe exclusively) as the violation of man's right of possession regarding each woman who may be his own legal wife (usually, one among many). On the contrary, adultery is not understood as it appears from the point of view of monogamy as established by the Creator. We know now that Christ referred to the 'beginning' precisely in regard to this argument (Mt. 19:8).[51]

Just as one must refer back to the original state of nature before the sin to understand the evil and yet toleration of divorce, so one must refer back to this state to understand the evil of slavery. The toleration of slavery can be interpreted in a way similar to the toleration of divorce in the Old Testament. In the same way, man was naked in the original justice because there was no possibility of extortion through lust. Clothing would be the product of the right

---

[51] John Paul II, *Blessed are the Pure of Heart* (Boston: St. Paul Editions, 1983), 94.

of nations in light of the fact of lust in society to preserve the personal freedom of sexuality. In these two states the powers of nature and their order are the same. What changes are the measures necessary to preserve this order because the loss of grace causes a disintegrity in the powers which human law tries to recover as much as possible.

St. Thomas rightly points out there could be no slavery in original justice because there man was created right. There could be no utilitarian ethic. Slavery entered in the state of original sin like divorce and polygamy, but not as goods. Slavery is always intrinsically evil. Slavery was the product of the right of nations. It was therefore the human law trying to determine the most expedient way to preserve certain goods of the economic order for the whole people given the economy of the time. One could certainly debate whether this was necessary to preserve the economy of the ancient world, but the fact is that most ancient peoples thought it was central to their survival economically.

If the positive law merely tolerated slavery, then it would be like Moses tolerating divorce. On the other hand, if the positive law established a right to slavery, then such a law is evil no matter what the economic goods are which result from it. Both Christ and the Church recall man to his first innocence and invite him to the New Life in which there are no slaves. Slavery is therefore always an evil against nature. St. Augustine spent must of the *City of God* trying to demonstrate that Rome fell because it was a society built on injustice, slavery, and cruelty.

St. Thomas goes even further. Without calling for emancipation he states flatly that the slaves have rights to eat, drink, and marry without the consent of their masters because slavery is only of the positive law, not of the natural law.

> Now just as nature seeks the preservation of the individual, so does it seek the preservation of the species by means of procreation; wherefore even as a slave is not so subject to his master as to not be at liberty to eat, sleep, and do such things as pertain to the needs of his body and without which his nature cannot be preserved, so he is not subject to him to the extent of being unable to marry freely, even without his master's knowledge or consent.[52]

St. Thomas' ideas reflect general scriptural teaching. Scripture can help us to understand why the Church tolerated

[52] Aquinas, *ST, Suppl.*, 52, 2, *corp.*

slavery for so many years. Why, for example, did St. Paul not require Philemon to immediately emancipate his slaves, but along with the Catholic tradition permit him to keep slaves? The answer to this question may also be applied to the bishops of the United States in their own toleration of slavery.

First, because of the widespread right of nations slavery had become an integral part of ancient culture. The Church sought to change this, but, lest the change be too abrupt, went slowly. "And nowhere does the slow, leavening power of Christianity manifest itself better than in the history of slavery."[52] St. Paul established the basic principles for the gradual recognition of the rights of slaves. He demanded that slavery should be treated only as an accident of history. Rather than completely disrupt society by calling for its abolition, St. Paul and the Church sought to transform it within. Slaves must be treated not as property, but as human persons. If the institution could not be abolished because of the situation of the secular society, then the practical evil effects of this institution could be changed by changing the attitude of the Christian parties who practiced it.

If it is true that the complete abolition of the institution of slavery seemed inevitable after the French Revolution and the Church then called for it, this was not because the Church needed the French Revolution to know that slavery was intrinsically evil, but rather because the French Revolution provided the needed social context of the secular culture in which the right of nations and therefore the economic basis of the culture had changed without causing complete social and economic chaos. In others words, the teaching of the French Revolution was merely the occasional cause, not the efficient cause of the teaching of the Church about the intrinsic evil of slavery. The Church did not change her teaching on the morality of slavery in any substantial way but finally implemented what had always been taught. Both the weight of Scripture and Tradition are firmly on the side of the intrinsic evil of slavery. The question was only when to implement this fully. This could only be done when economic chaos would not result. The change was only a change in prudent implementation, not a change in substance or form. It was a change from toleration of evil to abolition.

<hr />

[52] *A Catholic Commentary on Holy Scripture*, ed. Bernard Orchard, Edmund F. Sutcliffe, Reginald C. Fuller, and Ralph Russell (New York: Thomas Nelson and Sons, 1951), 821.

Religious Freedom

The same point could be made about the teaching of the Church on the subject of the freedom of religion. The *Syllabus of Errors* condemns religious freedom. *Dignitatis humanae* of Vatican II declares it to be a right. Professor Noonan reflects this fact when he quotes an observer at Vatican II who said that the Council had "reversed the teaching of the ordinary papal magisterium."[53] Professor Noonan interprets this fact as due to the culture.

> Only as social structures changed did moral mutation become possible, even if the change in social structures, as it might reasonably be argued, was owed at least in part to the perception that structures fostering liberty were more congruent with deeper insight into Christ.[54]

Then the summary he makes from the work of the famous moralist, Louis Vereecke would certainly be true: "moral theology is where the unchanged gospel encounters changing cultures."[55] He concludes: "Without those experiences, negative and positive, and without the elaboration of the ideal of Tocqueville and Murray, the changes made by Vatican II could not have occurred."[56]

Again, this change is only one of emphasis in the situation. The Church emphasizes another aspect of the Tradition in a homogeneous development. This homogeneous development of this doctrine depends on an understanding of *what the Church has always taught* about the relationship of the intellect to the will in the moral act. Freedom of choice in any human act is primarily an act of the will guided by reason.[57] Free choice demands the perfection of both the intellect and the will. St. Thomas, for example, uses the term *liberum arbitrium* to express the basis of any moral act. In this expression the *liberum* refers to the unfettered action of the will. The *arbitrium* refers to the action of the intellect perceiving truth.

---

[53] J. Robert Dionne, *The Papacy and the Church* (New York: Philosophical Library, 1987) 193; quoted in Noonan, "Development," 668.

[54] Noonan, "Development," 673.

[55] Ibid.; cf. footnote 6 above.

[56] Ibid., 674.

[57] "*Illa ergo quae rationem habent seipsa movent ad finem: quia habent dominium suorum actuum per liberum arbitrium, quod est facultas voluntatis et rationis*" (Aquinas, *ST*, I-II, 1, 2, corp.).

The condemnations of religious freedom in papal teaching such as those found in the *Syllabus of Errors*[58] speak of the relation of the freedom of religion to the part the act of the intellect plays in free choice. This condemns the error of indifferentism as enunciated by the Enlightenment. According to indifferentism one religious expression of the nature of God is as valid as another. All religions are equally true. The liberal state of the nineteenth century following the teachings of the French Revolution founded the freedom of religion on the philosophy that human reason was autonomous and perfect in discovering the truth of God. The state embodied this freedom in the perfect autonomous freedom of the citizens considered as a whole. Therefore to set any authority over the state in this regard was an alienation of man and also of the state. The Church therefore had no authority over autonomous human reason even in matters of religion. The state was the guardian of this liberty. Further, all religions were equally true provided they were useful to the state. Thus, the liberal ideas of the nineteenth century also affirmed that from the standpoint of truth in the intellect all religions were indifferent.

The *Syllabus of Errors* is squarely against this as not only theologically, but also philosophically inaccurate. Instead of proclaiming the autonomy of the state to define any truth about God, the *Syllabus* emphasizes the necessity of the authority of revelation to discover the full and complete truth about God. If the state has an obligation to preserve a confessional character, this is not because the state has a religious mission, but because in the climate of the time, this could be the only way to preserve the freedom of the Church to pursue the mission of Christ. The confessional state in the world following the Protestant Reformation of *cuius regio, eius religio* was the only means to preserve the right of the Church to teach, a right enjoyed by every citizen who did not infringe the natural law. The embodiment of the religious freedom of the Church in the confessional state was in no sense necessary, but merely an accident of history. The *Syllabus* also emphasizes that there is only one true religion from the standpoint of the intellect.

When Vatican II takes up the theme of religious liberty, then it affirms both the fact that there is no freedom of religion in the Church and that this freedom does not extend to indifferentism.

---

[58] H. Denzinger and A. Schonmetzer, eds., *Enchiridion Symbolorum*, 36th ed. (Barcinone: Herder, 1976), 1777-1779 (2077-2079).

So while the religious freedom which men demand in fulfilling their obligation to worship God has to do with freedom from coercion in civil society, it leaves intact the traditional Catholic teaching on the moral duty of individuals and societies towards the true religion and the one Church of Christ.[59]

If the *Syllabus of Errors* discusses freedom of religion from the point of view of the place the intellect plays in freedom of choice, *Dignitatis humanae* discusses the freedom of religion from the point of view of the part the will plays in freedom of choice. The former emphasizes the necessity of truth guiding moral choice. This necessity is emphatic to guide the freedom of the will in the act of faith which is the basis of true religious adherence. The latter emphasizes the freedom from external coercion which must be the basis for any responsible, moral choice.[60] This is especially true of the choice of faith, the most important choice in human life. Though the climate of the world may have been the occasion which led the Church to emphasize this or that aspect, it did not cause the Church to add something which contradicted a previous teaching made also by the Magisterium.

General Conclusion

The changes that Professor Noonan notes in the moral theology of the Catholic Church do not reflect a human nature that changes as to species. They also do not reflect changes that can even be attributed as such to the bodily constitution of individuals as is the case with the manner in which each person approaches the mean of virtues that have to do with the passions. They are in no sense formal changes then. They reflect a change of emphasis that is merely material in nature and due only to the social meaning of the good in question as in the case of money, or a change in emphasis due to a changing human law that will accept the teaching of the Church without causing social chaos as is the case with slavery and religious freedom. In the case of Pauline privilege, the change was only in the canonical extent of the jurisdiction of the pope. It seems that one is compelled to affirm

---

[59] Second Vatican Council, *Dignitatis humanae* (December 7, 1965), 1.

[60] For a more complete explanation of the ideas in this section, see Brian Mullady, "Religious Freedom: Homogeneous or Heterogeneous Development?" *The Thomist* 58, 1 (January, 1994), 93-108.

therefore that the moral teachings of the Catholic Church have changed over time, but only in a material and occasional sense by homogeneous development. One must also conclude that these examples in no way call into question the teaching of *Veritatis splendor* that there are norms that oblige *semper et pro semper.*[61]

---

[61] Cf. footnote 2 above.